Young Children Continue to Reinvent Arithmetic
— 2nd Grade —

IMPLICATIONS OF PIAGET'S THEORY

Constance Kamii
with Linda Leslie Joseph

Teachers College, Columbia University
New York and London

Published by Teachers College Press, 1234 Amsterdam Avenue, New York, NY 10027

Excerpts from the following material are reprinted by permission of the publisher:

Abbott, J. S., & Wells, D. W. *Mathematics today,* Teacher's Edition, Level 2, Red. Copyright © 1985 by Harcourt Brace Jovanovich, Inc.

Carpenter, T. P., Kepner, H., Corbitt, M. K., Lindquist, M. M., & Reys, R. E. (1980). Results and Implications of the Second NAEP Mathematics Assessments: Elementary Schools. *Arithmetic Teacher,* 27(8), p. 11.

Kouba, V. L., Brown, C. A., Carpenter, T. P., Lindquist, M. M., Silver, E. A., & Swafford, J. O. (1988). Results of the Fourth NAEP Assessment of Mathematics: Number, Operations, and Word Problems. *Arithmetic Teacher,* 35(8), p. 18.

Madell, R. (1985). Children's Natural Processes. *Arithmetic Teacher,* 32(7), p. 21.

National Council of Teachers of Mathematics. (1988, July). *Curriculum and evaluation standards for school mathematics* [draft]. National Council of Teachers of Mathematics.

Thompson, C. S., & Rathmell, E. C., (1988). NCTM's Standards for School Mathematics, K–12, *Arithmetic Teacher,* 35(9), p. 18.

Library of Congress Cataloging-in-Publication Data

Kamii, Constance.
  Young children continue to reinvent arithmetic—2nd grade:
  implications of Piaget's theory/Constance Kamii with Linda Leslie
  Joseph.
      p.   cm.—(Early childhood education series)
  Bibliography: p.
  Includes index.
  ISBN 0-8077-2958-2.—ISBN 0-8077-2957-4
  1. Arithmetic—Study and teaching (Elementary)   2. Number concept—
Study and teaching (Elementary)   3. Piaget, Jean, 1896–
I. Joseph, Linda Leslie.   II. Title.   III. Series.
QA135.5.K185   1989   89-4451
372.7—dc20   CIP

Manufactured in the United States of America
95   94   3   4   5   6

(Continued)

Contents

Preface

I wrote *Young Children Reinvent Arithmetic* (Kamii, 1985) about work I had done with first graders in 1980–1982. That project was carried out with one teacher, Georgia DeClark, in a suburb of Chicago. While it had been possible to develop a first-grade constructivist approach to arithmetic with only one teacher, I knew that my wish to create a second-grade program would require two teachers, one each in the first and second grades, who worked in the same school and had the support of the principal.

The reason for this requirement was that I did not want to work with second graders who had already become machine-like as a result of traditional instruction—children who could only count, store, retrieve, write, and mechanically follow rules called algorithms. Once children become followers of rules, such as the rule of adding columns from right to left, it is very hard to get them to do their own thinking. To develop a constructivist primary math program based on children's natural ability to think, I needed to work with second graders whose ability to think independently had been fostered in first grade.

I spent a considerable amount of time in and around Chicago in search of a public school principal who, rather than continuing to use the traditional textbook and workbook, was willing to try my ideas for following a class from the first through the second grade. Finding willing teachers was no problem, since I knew many teachers who were in a master's program at the University of Illinois at Chicago, where I was teaching at the time. Finding a principal, however, proved to be impossible. None whom I approached understood the nature of mathematics or of young children's thinking and always asked only one question: Can you promise good scores on the achievement test? The door to each school closed gently but tightly whenever I replied that I could not guarantee good test scores. I explained that achievement tests tapped mainly social (conventional) knowledge and that my emphasis was on logico-mathematical knowledge (i.e., children's thinking, which is explained in Chapter 1). I found that principals were not interested in children's thinking, only in better test scores.

A new element then appeared on the horizon. Milly Cowles, a friend and then the Dean of the School of Education at the University of Alabama at Birmingham, offered me a job. One of her arguments was that public schools in the South are much more open to universities than are those in the North. While she could not promise that any public school would be made available to me, she said that my chances of finding one were much better in Birmingham than in Chicago. I thus moved to Birmingham in January 1984.

By September 1984, I had a public school in which to work! All I wanted was 2 classes, but I got 10 instead—all of the K–2 classes in the whole school. (The 10 classes consisted of four at the kindergarten level and 3 each at grades 1 and 2).

The door to this school opened as a result of a lecture I gave about first-grade arithmetic in a summer course on Piaget's theory at the University of Alabama at Birmingham. At the end, I told the students, who were mostly teachers, that I was looking for a public school in which to extend this constructivist approach to second grade. One of the students in the class, Jackie Hughes, a first-grade teacher, came up and announced that she wanted to work with me and that her principal and fellow teachers might also be interested. She told me that her school, Hall-Kent Elementary, was in Homewood, a suburb of Birmingham.

A few weeks later, I heard from Jackie that her fellow teachers were indeed open and that I should talk with the principal, Gene Burgess. My conversation with him was surprisingly brief. I could hardly believe my ears when he gave me his response. He said his only regret was that, since I was interested only in the primary grades, the rest of the school would not have the benefit of my presence! He added, however, that it would be best to start in the lower grades, so that parents could be assured that their children would get traditional instruction before going to the middle school. This was the only principal I had talked with who did not ask about test scores. He was well aware of Piaget's work and thus understood my approach. Until then, I had not met a principal who was this autonomous, both intellectually and morally. (See Chapter 4 for an explanation of autonomy.)

I strongly believe in teachers' autonomy, so I said at the first meeting with the K–2 teachers that we would work together on a trial basis for a year and then decide if we wanted to continue working together. I asked for one thing, and that was the honest exchange of opinions. Open disagreement and exchanges are much more conducive to everybody's learning than polite compliance.

I visited each class about once a week, made comments on what I saw, offered suggestions, answered questions, and learned about the children in each classroom. We also had many meetings after school and on staff-development days, with all 10 teachers or with teachers of only one grade level. Most of the teachers were skeptical at the beginning; however, they were open and quick to see that the activities they had formerly provided for children were promoting only "right" answers and obedience.

In April 1985, there was a leadership conference of the Alabama Association for Supervision and Curriculum Development. Michael Gross, who was then the superintendent of the Homewood City Schools and a member of this association, asked that I and a teacher from each grade level make a presentation about our math program at this conference. Pam Burleson, Jackie Hughes, and Linda Joseph joined me in this presentation, and I was surprised by the conviction and excitement with which they "sold" their ideas, games, and other activities. I was particularly impressed by the precision with which they pointed out why their new activities were superior to the old ones still found in textbooks, workbooks, and packages of "manipulatives." The audience's positive response was also reassuring.

As I complete this book about second-grade arithmetic, it is the summer of 1988, and the constructivist primary math program has been in operation for 4 years at Hall-Kent School. (All the third-grade classes joined the constructivist program during the spring of 1985.) We still have many problems and unanswered questions, such as what to do with the teaching of measurement, what to do with slow learners, and so on. Nonetheless, I feel it is very important to share our results to this point, because I am distressed by the "testmania" and pressure for higher test scores that have swept across the country in recent years. With a sense of urgency to counteract this bandwagon, I decided to write this book at this time for three purposes: (1) to show that traditional arithmetic instruction goes counter to the way young children think; (2) to show that standardized achievement tests are misleading and harmful to young children; and (3) to show that there are better ways of teaching arithmetic in the primary grades, based on the scientific knowledge we now have about how young children construct logico-mathematical knowledge.

The book is divided into four parts. In the first part, I present the evidence supporting constructivism and the importance of social interaction in the classroom. I also show the way in which traditional instruction is based on erroneous assumptions about how young children learn arithmetic.

In the second part, I discuss goals and objectives of arithmetic instruction and explain how traditional instruction focuses only on surface behaviors. Specifically, in Chapter 4 I point out that traditional education unwittingly aims at blind obedience rather than critical, independent thinking. In Chapter 5, I argue in favor of defining objectives in terms of children's thinking and not in terms of getting them to write correct answers.

A strength of this book is the collaboration between one of the teachers involved in this project and myself as researcher. Part III, which focuses on classroom activities, was written with Linda Joseph, a teacher who strengthened my already deep and strong respect for good teachers. Linda invented the way of teaching place value and double-column addition described in Chapter 6. I do not deny the importance of Piaget's research and theory, which Linda studied especially during the entire summer of 1986 at the university. Without Linda's inventions, experimentation, and careful observations, however, Chapters 6 and 7 could not have been written.

Part IV deals with various approaches to evaluation. In Chapter 9, Linda gives her personal evaluation of children's learning, giving the kind of in-depth information that achievement tests cannot provide. In Chapter 10, I demonstrate that how we evaluate a program depends on our theory. If our theory states that "right" answers are all-important, we look only for children's correct answers, just as standardized achievement tests do. If, on the other hand, our theory emphasizes the process of reasoning and the foundation for further learning, we evaluate children's knowledge in very different ways that lead to different conclusions.

Like my earlier book, *Young Children Reinvent Arithmetic* (Kamii, 1985), this book is written not only for teachers of young children but also for administrators, curriculum specialists, and evaluators. I hope it will be used in courses on methods of teaching elementary mathematics, early childhood education, educational psychology, and evaluation.

The final point I would like to make is related to the teaching of language arts in early childhood education. This teaching has advanced considerably in recent years, and an increasing number of teachers are experimenting with how to encourage children to "invent" their own spelling in order to write their own ideas. This movement demonstrates that teachers can make progressive changes, even in an era of "back-to-basics" and "testmania." Encouraging children to construct knowledge from within is the diametric opposite of trying to impose isolated skills from the outside. Understanding the constructive process requires a Copernican revolution in educators' thinking, because it makes us shift the focus of our attention from what the teacher does to how children learn. I am optimistic that, in mathematics, too, educators are bound to begin a Copernican revolution. Testmania and back-to-basics seem to be parts of a stage through which educators have had to go. I hope this book will help them to go on to the next stage of their development.

Acknowledgments

The person who contributed the most to this book is Donald Eugene Burgess, Principal of Hall-Kent Elementary School in Homewood, Alabama. Most American principals in the 1980s are unwilling to discard textbooks and workbooks that present the kind of material covered by achievement tests. Gene Burgess was autonomous enough to have his own conviction about what is good for young children and about the scientific validity of Piaget's theory of the construction of knowledge. As Gene once remarked, many people are willing to follow, but *somebody* has to lead. He and his teachers made possible the work reported in this book.

I wish to express my appreciation to all the K–3 teachers of Hall-Kent School who were willing to reexamine the traditional way of teaching mathematics, reflect on their method of teaching arithmetic, and change their practice. These teachers are Pam Burleson, Joan Coker Burns, Dee Hellmers, Jackie Hughes, Sally Jones, Linda Joseph, Linda Klopack, Carol Lord, Leigh Chapple Martin, Russell Martin, Rhonda Merrill, Kay Nicholas, Mary-Martha Rhodes, Becky Salls, Karen Stevens, Susan Thompson, Gloria Wilkerson, and Carol Williamson. These teachers challenged and critiqued my ideas, invented activities for teaching arithmetic, observed and made suggestions, and helped me develop a constructivist approach to teaching arithmetic.

Janet Dickson, the music teacher, Angela Lewis, the special education teacher, and Sharon Wells, the librarian, also went out of their ways to be always helpful and supportive.

The teacher from whom I learned the most is Linda Joseph. She constantly invented and tried activities, welcomed visitors and talked with them, talked to classes at the university, conducted workshops for teachers in various parts of Alabama, made videotapes, studied Piaget's theory, and offered her reflections. She also agreed to write this book with me, contributing the more practical perspective of a classroom teacher.

Special thanks also go to Jackie Hughes, who took the initiative to invite me to Hall-Kent School for the first time. She, too, was autonomous enough to decide for herself that Piaget's research and theory merited exploration and possible commitment.

I am grateful to the young children of Hall-Kent School. I did not know that second graders could invent so many clever ways of adding and subtracting numbers. The remarkable thing is that, while these children are extraordinary, they think there is nothing unusual about their originality! They think of the traditionally "right" way (i.e., algorithms) as the "old-fashioned way," thereby strengthening my faith in future generations.

Also in the category of "hope for the future" is Vasha Rosenblum, a doctoral student and my research assistant at the University of Alabama at Birmingham. She assisted me in making test items, interviewed children individually, administered group tests, and was always ready to help with the countless details of research in public schools. Chapter 10 of this book could not have been written without her able assistance.

The principals and teachers of other schools who provided me with comparison groups deserve special thanks. They knew my position but at the same time realized that it was necessary to prove scientifically the desirability of any new approach to teaching. Had I not promised confidentiality to them, I would thank them individually by name.

The advice and support of colleagues at the University of Alabama at Birmingham have been invaluable. I am deeply indebted to Roberta Long, Gary Manning, Maryann Manning, and Bernice Wolfson for their readiness to help whenever there was a problem. A Cooperative Research and Development Grant from the School of Education helped me to work without financial support from external sources. Wayne Hamby kindly took most of the photographs that appear in this book.

Many of my colleagues and students at the university critically read parts of the manuscript and gave me advice. They are Linda Griffith, Roberta Long, Dee Morgan, Dode Morgan, Suzanne Stringer, and Bernice Wolfson. Ed Labinowics, of California State University at Northridge, and my sister, Mieko Kamii, of Wheelock College, devoted much time to specific parts of the manuscript.

This book could not have been written without the interest and generosity of Hermina Sinclair, of the University of Geneva. As my mentor since 1965, she has patiently explained the nature of logico-mathematical knowledge as well as other aspects of Piaget's difficult theory. She has critiqued my writing for years and has shared her vast knowledge and ideas with me. By coming to Birmingham in 1987, she enabled me to conceptualize the approach to evaluation reported in Chapter 10.

With the support of all these people and Robert Bumpus, superintendent of the Homewood City Schools, I feel encouraged to go on to create an approach to third grade mathematics and, once again, to have my expectations surpassed.

Young Children Continue to Reinvent Arithmetic
— 2nd Grade —

IMPLICATIONS OF PIAGET'S THEORY

Part I

THEORETICAL FOUNDATION

CHAPTER 1

Why Advocate Children's Reinventing Arithmetic?

Why do we want children to reinvent arithmetic, when we can simply tell them how to add, subtract, multiply, and divide? The answer to this question is presented at the end of this chapter and developed throughout this book. I will begin by quoting a few lines from Mathematics Today, a math textbook series published by Harcourt Brace Jovanovich, as an example of the theory on which math education is generally based today. I will then present Jean Piaget's theory related to primary arithmetic, critique the assumptions of traditional math education, and explain why I think that children will save time in the long run if they reinvent their own arithmetic instead of being taught how to produce correct answers.

The authors of the Mathematics Today series state in their Level 2 teacher's manual that their program "presents all basic number facts and computational skills," and that "all the basic operations are introduced by means of simple step-by-step models and algorithms, which often are accompanied by helpful illustrations" (Abbott & Wells, 1985, p. T26). After thus describing their way of teaching arithmetic, the authors go on to relate teaching to children's process of learning in the following way:

> The lessons in *Mathematics Today* have been structured carefully to ensure maximum learning. Learning always begins at the concrete level and then moves to the semiconcrete, to the symbolic, and finally to the abstract levels. Thus, students first learn to count real objects; then they count objects in pictures; then they use numbers; and finally they generalize number relationships. [p. T26]

The preceding statements are based on empiricist assumptions, according to which our knowledge has its source in the environment and is acquired by each child by internalization through the senses. Piaget's research and theory, called constructivism, have shown, however, that children acquire number concepts and operations by construction from the inside and not by internalization from the environment. This statement will be explained in the following section, beginning with a Piagetian task that clarifies this process.

3

CHILDREN'S ACQUISITION OF NUMBER CONCEPTS

The following task is a simplified version of several that are described by Inhelder and Piaget (1963). Two identical glasses and 30 to 50 wooden beads (or chips, beans, or other objects) are used in this task. The child is given one of the glasses, and the researcher takes the other glass. The adult then asks the child to drop a bead into his glass each time she drops one into hers. After about five beads have thus been dropped into each glass with one-to-one correspondence, the adult says, "Let's stop now, and watch what I am going to do." The researcher then drops one bead into her glass and suggests to the child, "Let's get going again." Each person drops about five more beads into his or her glass with one-to-one correspondence, until the adult says, "Let's stop."

The following is what has happened so far:

Adult: $1+1+1+1+1+1+1+1+1+1+1$
Child: $1+1+1+1+1 \quad +1+1+1+1+1$

The adult then asks, "Do we have the same number (or amount), or do *you* have more, or do *I* have more?"

Four-year-olds usually reply that the two glasses have the same amount. When we go on to ask, "How do you know we have the same amount?" the children explain, "Because I can see that we both have the same (amount)." Some 4-year-olds, however, reply that *they* have more, and when we ask them how they know that they have more, their explanation consists of only one word: "Because."

The adult goes on to ask, "Do you remember how we dropped the beads?" and 4-year-olds usually give all the empirical facts correctly: "Then you told me to stop, and you put one in your glass. Only you put one in your glass, and I watched 'cause you told me to wait. Then we got going again." In other words, 4-year-olds remember all the empirical facts correctly and base their judgment of equality on the empirical appearance of the two quantities.

By age 5 or 6, however, most children deduce logically that the experimenter has one more. When we ask these children how they know that the adult has one more, they invoke exactly the same empirical facts as the 4-year-olds.

If a child says that the adult's glass has one more bead, the researcher goes on to pose the next question: "If we continued to drop beads all day (or all night) in the same way (with one-to-one correspondence), do you think we will have the same number at the end, or will *you* have more, or will *I* have more?" Five- and 6-year-olds divide themselves into two groups at this point. Some answer in the way that adults would; that is, that there will *always* be one more in the researcher's glass. The others make empirical statements such as, "I don't know because we haven't done it yet," or, "You don't have enough beads to keep going all day."

The preceding task is one of the countless Piagetian experiments that demonstrate the difference between empirical knowledge and logico-mathematical knowledge. (Other tasks can be found in Kamii, 1985, Chapter 1.)

PIAGET'S THREE TYPES OF KNOWLEDGE

The difference between empirical knowledge and logico-mathematical knowledge can best be clarified by reviewing the distinction Piaget (1932/1965, 1950a, 1950b, 1950c, 1967/1971) made among three kinds of knowledge: physical, logico-mathematical, and social (conventional). Piaget's distinction among these three types of knowledge is based on their ultimate sources and modes of structuring.

Physical and Logico-Mathematical Knowledge

Physical knowledge is knowledge of objects in external reality. The color and weight of a bead are examples of physical properties that are *in* objects in external reality and can be known empirically by observation. The knowledge that a bead will fall into the glass when we let go of it is also an example of physical knowledge.

Logico-mathematical knowledge, on the other hand, consists of *relationships* created by each individual. For instance, when we are presented with a red bead and a blue one and think that they are "different," this difference is an example of logico-mathematical knowledge. The beads are indeed observable, but the *difference* between them is not. The difference is a *relationship* created mentally by each individual who puts the two objects into this relationship. The difference is neither *in* the red bead nor *in* the blue one, and if a person did not put the objects into this relationship, the difference would not exist for him.

Other examples of relationships the individual can create between the same beads are "similar," "the same in weight," and "two." It is just as correct to say that the red and blue beads are similar as it is to say that they are different. The relationship an individual puts the objects into is up to that individual. From one point of view the two beads are different, and from another point of view they are similar. If the individual wants to compare the weight of the two beads, he or she is likely to say that the objects are "the same" (in weight). If, on the other hand, the individual wants to think about the objects numerically, he or she will say that there are "two." The two beads are observable, but the "two-ness" is not. Number is a relationship created mentally by each individual.[1]

Physical knowledge is thus empirical knowledge that has its sources partly in objects. Logico-mathematical knowledge, on the other hand, is not empirical knowledge, as its source is in each individual's mind. Relationships must be created by each individual because relationships such as "different," "same," and "two" do not exist in the observable, external world. Children go on to elaborate their logico-mathematical knowledge by coordinating these simple relationships that they created between objects. For example, by coordinating the relationships of "same" and "different," children later become able to deduce that there are more beads in the world than red beads. It is likewise by coordinating the relationship between "two" and "two" that they later become able to deduce that $2 + 2 = 4$, and that $2 \times 2 = 4$.

Social Knowledge

The ultimate sources of social knowledge are conventions worked out by people. Examples of social knowledge are the fact that Halloween is October 31, that a tree is called "tree," and that tables are not to be stood upon. The main characteristic of social knowledge is that it is largely arbitrary in nature. The fact that a tree is called "tree" is an example of the arbitrariness of social knowledge. In another language, the same object is called by another name, since there is no physical or logical relationship between an object and its name. It follows that, for the child's acquisition of social knowledge, input from people is indispensable.

Implications for Arithmetic

To return to the task with beads and glasses, the knowledge that the beads stay in the glasses as separate entities (rather than becoming one

---

[1]I hasten to say that 2 is not a good number to choose to illustrate the logico-mathematical nature of number because it is a perceptual number. Piaget referred to small numbers up to 4 or 5 as "perceptual numbers" because small numbers of objects, such as "oo" and "ooo," can easily be distinguished from one another at a glance, perceptually. When seven or more objects ("ooooooo" and "oooooooo," for example) are presented, however, it is impossible to distinguish them by perception alone.

The number 2 can also be a logico-mathematical number for an adult who has constructed the system of logico-mathematical numbers. I chose the number 2 in this example in spite of the problem of perceptual numbers because, with two beads, I could illustrate other simple relationships such as "different," "similar," and "the same in weight."

continuous quantity like drops of water) is an example of empirical, physical knowledge. On the other hand, words such as *more* and *one, two, three,* and *four,* which children often use, belong to social knowledge. The numerical thinking, however, which is the most important part of the task, belongs to logico-mathematical knowledge, which has its source in each child's head.

The distinction among the three kinds of knowledge is essential to explaining why most 4-year-olds say that the two glasses have the same quantity. When children have not yet constructed the logico-mathematical relationships of number in their heads, all they can get from the experiment is physical, empirical knowledge. This is why 4-year-olds can remember the empirical facts of dropping all the beads except one with one-to-one correspondence. This one-to-one correspondence, however, is only empirical, and 4-year-olds judge the quantity of beads also empirically. This is why they say that the two glasses have the same amount and explain, "I can *see* they have the same amount."

By age 5 or 6, however, most children have constructed the logico-mathematical relationship of one-to-one correspondence and can deduce from the same empirical facts that the experimenter has one more bead. This system of relationships takes many years to construct, however, and the child who has number concepts up to 10 or 15 does not necessarily have concepts of 50, 100, or more. This is why many 5- and 6-year-olds who can judge that the experimenter has one more bead fall back on empirical knowledge when asked what would happen if the one-to-one correspondence were continued a long time. When they later construct a larger system of numbers, they become able to deduce, like us, that there will *always* be one more in the experimenter's glass, no matter how many beads are dropped with one-to-one correspondence.

Traditionally, mathematics educators have not made the distinction among the three kinds of knowledge and believe that arithmetic must be internalized from objects (as if it were physical knowledge) and people (as if it were social knowledge). They overlook the most important part of arithmetic, which is logico-mathematical knowledge.

TWO VIEWS OF HOW CHILDREN LEARN ARITHMETIC

Our ideas about how to teach arithmetic depend on our understanding of how children learn it. To the extent that we understand how children learn arithmetic, we can try to facilitate their learning. If, however, our theory is wrong, we may even teach it in ways that interfere with children's learning. Let us, therefore, examine two different views on this subject.

The theory of learning quoted from the Mathematics Today series at the beginning of this chapter is held by almost all the authors of other math series as well. Learning is divided into four basic levels, as follows:

1. Concrete level: counting real objects
2. Semiconcrete level: counting objects in pictures
3. Symbolic level: using written numbers
4. Abstract level: generalizing number relationships

This theory is based on empiricist assumptions, according to which all knowledge is acquired by internalization from the environment. The theory begins with the child's learning to count real objects; however, counting involves mostly social knowledge rather than logico-mathematical knowledge. This is why 4-year-olds may know all the words necessary for counting but use these words to represent their prelogical, or preoperational, knowledge. We will shortly see two examples of this.

I believe that traditional math educators' theory of learning suffers from a lack of differentiation between abstraction and representation, on the one hand, and between representation with personal symbols and with conventional signs, on the other. I will discuss these in turn.

Abstraction

There are two kinds of abstraction, according to Piaget (1950, 1967/1971): empirical or simple, and reflective or constructive.

In empirical abstraction, all the child does is focus on a certain property of the object and ignore the others. For example, when he or she abstracts the color of a bead, the child simply ignores the other properties such as the weight and the material of which the bead is made.

Reflective or constructive abstraction, by contrast, involves the child's construction of relationships between or among objects. Relationships, as stated earlier, do not have an existence in external reality. The similarity or difference between two beads exists only in the minds of those who create it mentally.

The reader may have noted that empirical abstraction is involved in the child's acquisition of physical knowledge, while constructive abstraction is involved in the acquisition of logico-mathematical knowledge.[2]

Traditional math educators often say that a number is a property of a set, and that a set of eight objects, for example, has the property of

---

[2] Having made the theoretical distinction between empirical and constructive abstraction, Piaget (1967/1971) went on to say that, in the psychological reality of the child, one kind of

"eight." To me, this is a serious misconception. Sets do not *do* anything by themselves, such as "have" a property. The action of "having" is done by the child, who constructs number concepts and imposes them on sets. This statement can be clarified by presenting Piaget's theory of number, by which he proposes that children construct number concepts by synthesizing two kinds of relationships they make: order and hierarchical inclusion (Gréco, Grize, Papert, & Piaget, 1960).

Let us look first at the relationship of order. All teachers of young children have seen the common tendency among children to count objects by skipping some and counting some more than once. When given eight objects, for example, a 4-year-old who can recite the series of numbers correctly from 1 to 10 may end up claiming that there are 10 things by "counting" them as shown in Figure 1.1a. This tendency indicates that children do not feel the logical necessity of putting the objects into an ordered relationship to make sure they do not skip any or count the same ones more than once. The only way an individual can be sure of not overlooking any or counting the same object more than once is by putting them into the relationship of order. The objects do not have to be put in a *spatial* order, however; what is important is that the individual order them *mentally*, as shown in Figure 1.1b.

If ordering were the children's only mental action on the objects, they

Figure 1.1. Counting (a) without ordering the objects and (b) by mentally ordering the same objects.

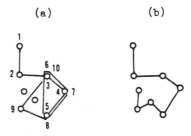

From *Number in Preschool and Kindergarten* by C. Kamii, 1982, National Association for the Education of Young Children.

---

abstraction cannot take place without the other. For example, the child could not construct the relationship "different" if all the objects in the world were identical. Conversely, the child could not construct physical knowledge without a logico-mathematical framework. To note that a certain fish is red, for example, the child needs a classification scheme by which to distinguish "red" from "all other colors." He or she also needs a classification scheme by which to distinguish "fish" from all the other kinds of known objects. A logico-mathematical framework is thus necessary for empirical abstraction, because children could not "read" facts from external reality if each fact remained an isolated bit of knowledge, with no relationship to the knowledge already built in an organized fashion.

would still not quantify the collection numerically. For example, after counting eight objects arranged in linear order, as shown in Figure 1.2a, 4-year-olds usually state that there are eight. If we then ask them to show us eight, they sometimes point to the last one (the eighth object). This behavior indicates that, for these children, the words *one, two, three,* and so on are names for individual elements in a series, like *Monday, Tuesday,* and *Wednesday.* When asked how many there are, children think they are expected to say the last word in the series. To quantify the collection of objects numerically, they have to put the objects in a relationship of hierarchical inclusion. This relationship, shown in Figure 1.2b, means that children *mentally* include "one" in "two," "two" in "three," "three" in "four," and so on. When presented with eight objects, they can quantify the collection numerically only if they can put all the objects into a single relationship, thus synthesizing order and hierarchical inclusion.

I hope the foregoing has demonstrated why I say that sets do not "have" a number property and that there is no such thing as a number concept at the so-called concrete level, as stated in the Mathematics Today series. Number concepts are always abstract because they are created by each child through constructive abstraction. Having explained my belief that the concrete level of learning numbers does not exist, I turn next to the equally dubious semiconcrete and symbolic levels. It is necessary for this examination to present Piaget's theory of representation.

Representation

The first point to be made about representation is that, according to Piaget (Piaget & Inhelder, 1966/1969), the word *eight* or a picture of eight

Figure 1.2. The term *eight* used (a) to refer only to the last element and (b) to refer to all the elements, with the mental structure of hierarchical inclusion.

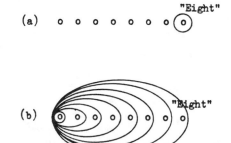

From *Young Children Reinvent Arithmetic* (p. 12) by C. Kamii, 1985, New York, Teachers College Press. Copyright © 1985 by Teachers College, Columbia University.

cookies does not represent the idea of "eight." Representation is what children do, and not what the word or picture does. If children have constructed the idea of "eight" (through constructive abstraction), they will represent this idea to themselves when presented with the word *eight* or a picture of eight objects. If not, they will give a prenumerical meaning to the word or picture.

Piaget (Piaget & Inhelder, 1966/1969) made a distinction between symbols and signs, which is illustrated in Figure 1.3. This distinction shows that there is no such thing as a semiconcrete level of learning numbers. Examples of *symbols* are pictures, tally marks, and fingers used as counting devices. The characteristics of symbols are (1) that they bear a figurative resemblance to the idea being represented and (2) that they can be invented by each child. Symbols require no input from other people to understand, and 4-year-olds can invent symbols such as those shown in Figure 1.4 (Sinclair, Siegrist, & Sinclair, 1983). Once children have con-

Figure 1.3.   Examples of the Piagetian distinction between symbols and signs, and their independent relationship to the expression of logico-mathematical knowledge.

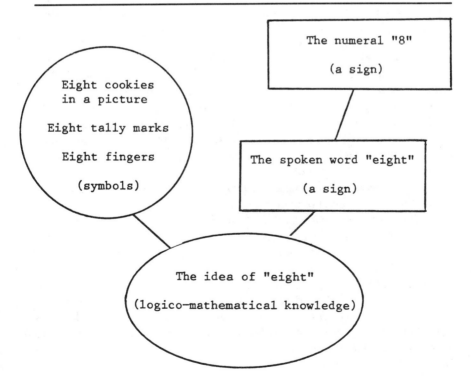

Figure 1.4.   Symbols invented by a 4-year-old to represent numerical ideas.

structed the idea of "three" or "eight," through constructive abstraction, they invent their own symbols to represent this logico-mathematical knowledge. *Signs* such as the word *eight*, on the other hand, belong to social (conventional) knowledge, and require input from people. Signs thus have different sources and are not more "advanced" than symbols. Both symbols and signs can be used simultaneously by children in the expression of logico-mathematical knowledge.

It follows from this discussion that all the pictures in workbooks and work sheets are unnecessary for children's learning of arithmetic, because children do not get logico-mathematical knowledge *from* pictures. If they need something to count, they will make their own symbols by drawing sticks or using their fingers.

I will now discuss the symbolic or third level of learning proposed in the terminology of the Mathematics Today series. As Figure 1.3 illustrates, written numerals were made to represent spoken words. It can be understood from this figure that if the spoken word *eight* gets its meaning from one's logico-mathematical knowledge, the written numeral 8 does, too. The so-called symbolic level of written numerals (in the terminology of Mathematics Today) is, therefore, not a level that grows out of the so-called semiconcrete level of pictures.

We now arrive at the final level proposed by traditional math educators—the abstract level of generalizing number relationships. The task of dropping beads into two glasses, as well as many other tasks, demonstrates that the child constructs numerical relationships through constructive abstraction, and not by going through the semiconcrete or symbolic level. Some 5- and 6-year-olds who cannot count well or read numerals say that there would *always* be one more bead in the experimenter's glass, even if beads were dropped into the glasses, with one-to-one correspondence, *forever.* Because many traditional math educators seem not to have heard of constructive abstraction, or have chosen to ignore it, they focus only on representation and overlook the importance of abstraction.

"Number Facts"

We saw at the beginning of this chapter that the Mathematics Today series claims to present "all basic number facts and computational skills" (Abbott & Wells, 1985, p. T26). I hope I have demonstrated that there is no such thing as a "number fact." A fact is observable and is empirical knowledge, but number concepts are not observable. If "eight" is a relationship created by each child, "8 + 8" is a relationship based on two relationships and is also created mentally by each child, through constructive abstraction.

According to Piaget (Piaget & Inhelder, 1948/1967), even facts are "read" from reality differently by children at different levels of development. The experiment on memory described in my earlier book (Kamii, 1985, pp. 69–72) illustrates this statement.

In this experiment, the children, who ranged in age from 4 to 6½, were shown a model consisting of three rows of six blue chips each. The three rows consisted of the following subgroups: 3 + 3, 1 + 2 + 3, and 1 + 5. The children were asked to use a set of six red chips to find out if the red chips covered up each row. After observing that they could indeed cover up each row with their red chips, the children were asked to reproduce the model from memory. Only one child, the oldest, reproduced the model exactly, and 4-year-olds produced rows that differed greatly in number, such as 12, 8, and 9. Those between the two extremes produced arrangements such as 15, 13, and 13; 7, 5, and 6; and 4, 4, and 8. Even observed facts are read and remembered differently by children of different developmental levels.

Algorithms

As previously noted, the authors of Mathematics Today claim that in their program "all the basic operations are introduced by means of simple step-by-step models and algorithms, which often are accompanied by helpful illustrations" (Abbott & Wells, 1985, p. T26). I will show in Chapters 2, 6, and 10 that these models and algorithms are rules imposed by adults, which children can explain only by saying, "The teacher told us to do it this way."

WHY CHILDREN SHOULD REINVENT ARITHMETIC

I can cite three reasons for advocating children's reinventing arithmetic. The first is that arithmetic instruction is not working today because

traditional math educators' theory of how children learn arithmetic is erroneous. For example, it has been known since 1980 that place value is
finally mastered by only half of the children in fourth grade (M. Kamii,
1980, 1982). Other researchers have repeatedly confirmed this conclusion as will be discussed in Chapter 2. In Chapter 10 of this book it will
also be shown that only 23% of traditionally instructed second graders
could explain the reasoning involved in addition with "regrouping." Since
this was the percentage among a group of upper-middle-class children,
the proportion can be expected to be even lower in less advantaged
groups.

The second argument is that, when children reinvent arithmetic, they
become more competent than traditionally instructed children. This
statement is elaborated upon in Chapter 10, in which the results of constructivist and traditional instruction are compared at the end of second
grade.

The third reason is that the procedures children invent are rooted in
the depth of their intuition and their natural ways of thinking. If we encourage them to develop their own ways of thinking rather than requiring
them to memorize rules that do not make sense to them, children develop a better cognitive foundation as well as confidence. Children who
are confident will learn more in the long run than those who have been
taught in ways that make them distrust their own thinking.

Traditional instruction imposes techniques (algorithms) that are foreign
to young children's ways of thinking. For example, if we tell them that
the way to do 13 + 13 is 3 + 3 + 10 + 10, this rule goes counter to
the way they think. Children think about 13 as 10 and 3, not as 3 and 10.
This is why they universally add the tens first and then the ones, when
they are encouraged to invent their own procedures.

Upon hearing the preceding statements, some people conclude that I
want children to reinvent everything in mathematics, including algebra.
I think the role of instruction must increase as children grow older. In
the primary grades, however, I firmly believe that children must construct one level after another of their own if they are to have a solid
foundation for further learning. Children who are excited about explaining their own ideas will go much farther in the long run than those who
can only follow somebody else's rules and respond to unfamiliar problems
by saying, "I don't know how to do it because I haven't learned it in
school yet."

CHAPTER 2

Place Value and Double-Column Addition

Place value here refers to the fact that in the number 333, for example, the first 3 means three hundred (or three hundreds), the second 3 means thirty (or three tens), and the third 3 means three. Place value is obviously important, because children who do not understand it will be seriously handicapped in adding, subtracting, multiplying, and dividing large numbers.

Place value is now taught in first grade, and again in every subsequent grade of elementary school. Research has shown, however, that most children think that the 1 in 16 means one, until third or fourth grade. These findings were first reported by Mieko Kamii (1980, 1982) and confirmed by other researchers, as stated in Chapter 1.

In this chapter, I will explain why traditional instruction is so unsuccessful in this area. I will first summarize the recent research on children's understanding of place value and will then focus on how children think about "tens and ones" independently of their interpretation of our written system of numeration. In the third section, I will relate instructional practices to these findings from research.

CHILDREN'S UNDERSTANDING OF PLACE VALUE

Ross's Study

Ross (1986) built on Mieko Kamii's (1980, 1982) work, as well as that of Resnick (1982, 1983) and others, in a comprehensive study of children's understanding of place value. The subjects in her study consisted of 60 children, 15 each in Grades 2 through 5. Her sampling was unusual in that she randomly selected children from 33 classrooms "from the grade level enrollment lists of five elementary schools in Butte County, California. . . . The schools were selected to represent urban and rural communities, public and private funding, and diversity with respect to the mathematics textbook series used, school size, and social class" (Ross, 1986, p. 3).

In individual interviews, Ross presented each child with 25 sticks (tongue depressors). She asked the child to count out the sticks and "write down the number." She then circled the digit in the ones place (5) and asked, "Does this part have anything to do with how many sticks you have?" After the child's response and other specific answers, she indicated the digit in the tens place (2) and asked the same questions about the meaning of the numeral 2.

The four levels of response she found in this task were as follows:

Level 1. While a whole two-digit numeral represents the whole numerical quantity of a collection of objects, the child indicates that the individual digits in a two-digit numeral have no numerical meaning. . . .

Level 2. While the whole numeral represents the whole quantity, the child *invents* numerical meanings for the individual digits; the invented meanings are not related to place-value notions of groupings into tens and/or ones. . . .

Example: In 25 sticks the "5" means groups containing five sticks, "2" means groups containing two sticks. . . .

Level 3. While the whole numeral represents the whole quantity, the individual digits have meanings related to groups of tens or ones but the child has only a partial or confused idea of how this all works. The sum of the parts need not equal the whole.

Type A. The place-value meanings assigned to the individual digits are incomplete or inconsistent.

Type B. Both individual digits mean ones.

Type C. The child reverses the meanings of the digits; the right digit means groups of ten and the left digit means ones.

Level 4. The whole numeral in a two-digit numeral represents a whole quantity of objects. The individual digits represent the partitioning of the whole quantity into groups of ten units (the tens digit) and a part composed of units (the ones digit). The whole must equal the sum of the parts. [Ross, 1986, p. 5]

Ross's (1986) findings are reported in Table 2.1. As can be seen in the following statement, she found essentially the same thing as Mieko Kamii (1980, 1982): "While every child in the study was able to determine the number of sticks and write the appropriate numeral, not until grade 4 did half the children demonstrate that they knew that the 5 represented five sticks and the 2 represented 20 sticks" (Ross, 1986, p. 5).

Silvern and Kamii's Study

Silvern interviewed 98 lower-middle-class children in the second, third, and fourth grades in three small rural towns in eastern Alabama.

TABLE 2.1: Performance on Sticks Task
(by Number of Children)

Grade	Level of Performance			
	1	2	3	4
2	5	2	5	3
3	7	1	2	5
4	0	7	0	8
5	1	4	0	10
Total	13	14	7	26

n = 15 for each grade
chi-square = 30.1; df = 9
p < .0004

From "The Development of Children's Place-Value
Numeration Concepts in Grades Two through Five," by
S. H. Ross, 1986, paper presented at the annual
meeting of the American Educational Research
Association, San Francisco, p. 6. Reprinted by
permission.

Two of the tasks he gave concerned place value and addition with regrouping.

Silvern's place-value task was similar to Ross's, but he used 16 chips.
He showed a card to each child on which he had written the numeral 16,
presented along with a pile of 16 poker chips. He then said, "I have
written the number 16 on this card, and I think I have 16 chips here.
Would you count them and make sure?" After the child counted the
chips, Silvern circled the 6 in 16 and asked, "Do you see this part? What
does it mean?" He asked the child to demonstrate the answer using the
chips. He then circled the 1 in 16 and asked the child, "And this part,
what does it mean?" Again, he asked the child to demonstrate the answer
with chips. If the child showed only one chip, Silvern pointed to the
remaining nine chips and asked, "What about these? Is this the way it's
supposed to be, or is there something strange?"

The children's responses to the questions regarding tens were grouped
into the following three categories:

1. The child said that the 1 in 16 meant one and showed 1 chip.
2. The child said that the 1 in 16 meant one ten and still showed 1
   chip.
3. The child said that the 1 in 16 meant ten (or one ten or tens) and
   showed 10 chips.

The percentages of the three categories that were found at each grade
level are reported in Table 2.2. It can be observed in this table that the

TABLE 2.2; Performance on Place Value Task
(in Percentage)

Grade	n	Category		
		1	2	3
2	26	85.0	7.5	7.5
3	24	67.0	4.0	29.0
4	48	59.0	6.0	35.0

proportion of third graders who said the 1 in 16 meant ten was 29%, which is essentially the same as previous findings. However, the proportion in fourth grade who made this statement was only 35%, as compared to the 50% reported in previous studies.

Silvern tested the same children on addition by writing the following problem on a card:

$$\begin{array}{r} 37 \\ +48 \\ \hline \end{array}$$

He asked each child to solve this problem in his or her head, and he grouped their responses into the following three categories:

1. The child made no attempt to solve the problem or gave a completely wrong response (e.g., 715).
2. The child wrote the numeral 75 (or 74 or 76).
3. The child wrote the numeral 85 (or 84 or 86).

As can be seen in Table 2.3, many second graders had trouble "regrouping" the ten, but almost all the children could do the addition problem by the third grade, using the algorithm taught at school. Since this problem would have been too easy for fourth graders, it was not given to them.

It is clear from this study that, while third graders can get correct answers to two-digit addition problems involving so-called regrouping, most of them think that the 1 in 16 means one. I will go on to a similar study I conducted with subjects from a different socioeconomic group.

C. Kamii's Study

In the spring of 1987, I interviewed 32 second graders in two classes and 40 third graders in two classes, in two public schools in a suburb of Birmingham, Alabama. This school system is known to produce very high test scores. The fact that there were only 16 or 20 children in each class

TABLE 2.3: Performance on Addition Task
(Percentage)

Grade	n	Category		
		1	2	3
2	26	42.0	31.0	27.0
3	24	8.4	0	91.6

reflects the middle- to upper-middle-class status of the area served by these schools.

I used exactly the same procedure as Silvern did in the place-value task but used two cards, one with 16 and one with 54 written on it. The proportion of children who said that the 1 in 16 meant ten, and that the 5 in 54 meant fifty are given in Table 2.4. As can be seen, the percentages for the 5 in 54 are higher than those for the 1 in 16. The reason is probably that some children thought about tens and ones while dealing with the 1 in 16 and improved their performance on the next task.

The problems used for the addition task were the following:

$$\begin{array}{r} 25 \\ +28 \end{array} \qquad \begin{array}{r} 39 \\ +28 \end{array}$$

The proportions of children who got the correct answers were 84% in second grade and 100% in third grade. Thus it can be said once again that the ability to produce correct answers in double-column addition by following the algorithm does not mean that children understand place value.

Bednarz and Janvier's Study

A comprehensive study conducted by Bednarz and Janvier (1982) in Montreal consisted of a large variety of ingenious tasks, of which I will give only one example here. The portion described here involved 75 third graders and 45 fourth graders in a middle-class and an upper-class school. (The entire study involved many other children, some in first grade, and others who were tested in groups.)

In an interview with each individual, a researcher scattered on the table the 20 tags shown in Figure 2.1 and said, "I have this number [writ-

TABLE 2.4: Performance on Place-Value Task
(Percentage)

Grade	n	1 of 16	5 of 54
2	32	16.0	28.0
3	40	30.0	57.5

Figure 2.1.   The tags provided by Bednarz and Janvier in their task.

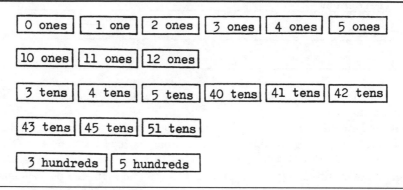

ing 402 and reading it] and that one [writing 513 and reading it]. I'm thinking of a number that is bigger than this one [402] and smaller than this one [513], a number which is in between" (p. 45). (The number was 445.)

The interviewer then showed a sheet of paper to the child on which the following writing appeared (p. 45):

402   ?   513

your number

_____
_____
_____
_____
_____
_____

The instructions were

> You must find out the number I have in mind but you must use the tags to make the number. You may use as many tags as you need. When you write down your number in this column (*showing on the sheet*) you must show me the tags you used to make it, [and] I will then tell you if my number is bigger or smaller than yours. [p. 45]

If the child could not guess the number, he or she was told the answer and asked to make the number with the tags. To test the child's ability to understand place value, the researchers also asked the child to write various other numbers made with a variety of tags, such as the number made by a tag saying "42 tens," by two tags saying "4 tens," and by a tag saying "12 ones."

As can be seen in Table 2.5, only 27% of the third graders and 44 percent of the fourth graders gave evidence of understanding the hundreds, tens, and ones (category 3 performance). The children in category 1 used all the numerals, without paying any attention to the written parts of the tags. For example, they wrote 4405 when presented with the following three tags: 4 ones, 40 tens, and 5 hundreds. The children in category 2 looked for tens first and then for ones, as if tens and ones stood only for the order of writing numerals. For example, to make 445, they took 4 tens and 5 ones and then looked for 4 hundreds, which did not exist.

Bednarz and Janvier (1982) repeatedly refer in their article to specific parts of the school curriculum and point out its shortcomings. Because they probed into children's ideas about hundreds, tens, and ones with a

TABLE 2.5: Performance on Tags Task (Percentage)

	Grade 3	Grade 4
1. Work exclusively with the digit (numerical part) of the tags without paying attention to words: ones, tens, hundreds; no meaning given to symbols ones, tens, hundreds.	41	35
2. Ones, tens, and hundreds are mainly related to the idea of order in the writing (and not to the idea of grouping).	30	21
3. Give a meaning to ones, tens, and hundreds in terms of groupings.*	27	44
4. Unclassifiable	2	0

*Category 3 represents good understanding.

large variety of tasks involving objects and pictures, their conclusions are
particularly convincing. Even in the third and fourth grades, they say,
most children do not understand place value. They point out, however,
that the hundreds cause much more difficulty in all the tasks than the
tens.

Cauley's Study

A study by Cauley (1988) is different from the preceding ones in that
it involves subtraction. It also reveals children's inability to understand
place value, even while being able to produce correct answers.

In a suburban public school and an urban Catholic school in Delaware,
Cauley (1988) identified 34 out of 90 children in the second and third
grades who were highly proficient in subtraction involving "borrowing."
Cauley interviewed these 34 children individually about their reasoning
and the meaning of what they had written. Two examples of their work
are given in Figure 2.2. One of the questions she asked was, "Before you
borrowed you had [56] and after you borrowed you had this much [the
minuend and all the borrowing.marks were circled]; did you have more
before you borrowed, or after you borrowed, or was it the same?" (p.
203).

Only 41% of the 34 children who used the algorithm proficiently replied that the number was the same after borrowing, while 32% said they
had more before borrowing and 24% said they had more afterward.

A common finding from the studies cited in this section is that children
in the primary grades and beyond often think that the 2 in 25 means two
and that the 1 in 16 means one. Why do they go on reading every digit
as signifying ones, after all the repeated instruction on place value in
every grade of elementary school? This question will be addressed in the
following section.

Figure 2.2. Children's written work in Cauley's study of subtraction involving "borrowing."

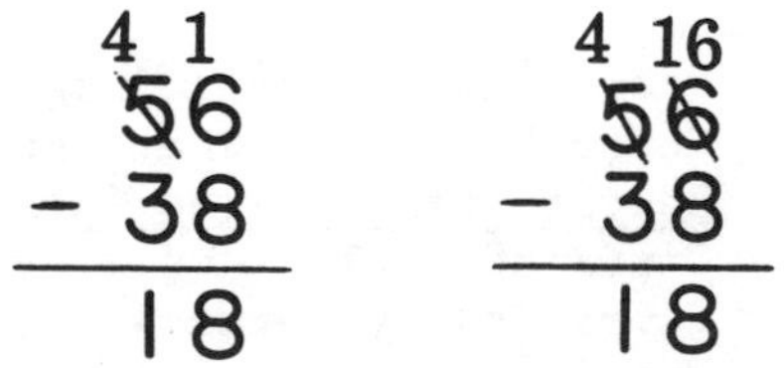

GRADUAL CONSTRUCTION OF A SYSTEM OF TENS

As we saw in Chapter 1, in the task of dropping beads into two glasses, and later in the discussion of order and hierarchical inclusion, first graders are in the process of constructing the system of ones. When they say the number 32, for example, they are thinking about 32 ones, not about 3 tens and 2 ones.

To be able to think about 32 as comprising 3 tens and 2 ones, the child has to construct a second system—that of tens—on the system of ones, by constructive abstraction. This is illustrated in Figure 2.3. Just as the system of ones cannot be put into the child's head from the environment, the system of tens cannot be transmitted from objects and people, either. While written numerals are social knowledge, and the decision to use ten as the base is also a convention, the hierarchical part-whole *relationships* shown in Figure 2.3 belong to logico-mathematical knowledge.

Like the system of ones, the system of tens involves the child's synthesizing the relationships of order and hierarchical inclusion. In the system of tens, too, the child has to order the ones mentally, and include "one" in "two," "two" in "three," and so on; but the ones in this system are actually tens. It is hard enough for young children to construct the system of ones. Mentally making a unit out of ten ones is a Herculean task that is very hard for adults to appreciate.

In order for children to become able to understand the system of tens, they must have enough time to construct the first system (of ones). The first system would otherwise not become solid enough to serve as the foundation for the second system (of tens). This is why it is impossible for first graders to understand place value, as I insisted in my earlier book, *Young Children Reinvent Arithmetic* (Kamii, 1985). This is also why so many children continue to read every digit as representing ones, in spite of the repeated instruction on place value they receive year after year.

I will discuss in this section two studies that demonstrate young children's thinking by ones and their gradual construction of the system of tens in grades 2 through 5.

Figure 2.3.   The system of tens constructed on the system of ones.

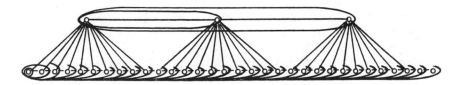

Ross's Study

The first study, by Ross (1986), is part of the comprehensive study al-
luded to earlier. Ross worked in individual interviews with the same children described earlier (15 children each in Grades 2 through 5). She
presented each child with 48 lima beans and 9 one-ounce plastic cups and
asked that he or she put 10 beans in each cup. The unused 5 cups were
then set aside, so that there remained on the table 8 loose beans and 4
cups, each containing 10 beans.

Ross then asked the child how many beans were on the table alto-
gether, and inquired, "How do you know?" She observed the following
three levels of responses in this task:

1. The children were simply unable to quantify the grouped objects.
2. The children counted mostly by ones, rather than using any of the
   more efficient methods found at level 3.
3. The children counted by tens and then added the eight loose
   beans. Some of them used implicit or explicit multiplication, saying, "Four tens is 40," or "Four times 10 is 40."

It can be seen in Table 2.6 that only nine second graders (60%) counted
the beans by tens, in spite of the fact that they had put the beans into the
cups in groups of ten. It can also be seen that the proportion of children

TABLE 2.6: Performance on Beans Task
(by No. of Children)

| | Level of Performance | | |
Grade	1	2	3
2	2	4	9
3	0	4	11
4	1	1	13
5	0	0	15
Total	3	9	48

n = 15 for each grade
chi-square = 11.0, df = 6; p < .0884

From "The Development of Children's Place-Value
Numeration Concepts in Grades Two through Five," by
S. H. Ross, 1986, paper presented at the annual
meeting of the American Educational Research
Association, San Francisco, p. 17. Reprinted by
permission.

who counted by tens increased steadily as they grew older. This under-scores the fact that children think in terms of ones until they construct the system of tens.

Next, in an effort to test conservation, Ross (1986) spilled one of the four cups of beans onto the table, so that there would be 10 beans in each of three cups, plus 18 loose beans. She then asked, "Do you think there are now more beans or fewer than there were before?" After the child's response, she asked, "How do you know?"

In this test, the children at level 1, the nonconservers, remained con-vinced that the total quantity was either more or less when one cup of beans was spilled. (Conservation refers to a person's ability to deduce that a quantity has stayed the same after its appearance has been changed, and to explain why.) The level 2 children, by contrast, changed their minds from nonconservation to conservation when the experimenter went on to ask one more question: "How many beans are there now, if there were 48 before?" At level 3 were the solid conservers, who needed no prompting to deduce that the quantity was the same.

As can be seen in Table 2.7, the second graders proved to be at a surprisingly low level of performance on this conservation task. Six of them (40%) turned out to be solid nonconservers, and four (27%) turned out to be at level 2, indicating that 4 tens and 8 ones are not the same for them as 3 tens and 18 ones. It can be seen in this table, too, that the proportion of solid conservers increases with age. This, too, is evidence of the gradual construction of the system of tens on the system of ones.

TABLE 2.7: Performance on Conservation Task
(by No. of Children)

Grade	Level of Performance		
	1	2	3
2	6	4	5
3	3	1	11
4	1	3	11
5	0	1	14
Total	10	9	41

n = 15 for each grade
chi-square = 15.6, df = 6; p < .0163

From "The Development of Children's Place-Value Numeration Concepts in Grades Two through Five," by S. H. Ross, 1986, paper presented at the annual meeting of the American Educational Research Association, San Francisco, p. 19. Reprinted by permission.

Kamii's Study

Another study (Kamii, 1986), conducted in Geneva, Switzerland, also demonstrates the gradual construction of the system of tens between second and fifth grade. I interviewed 100 children in grades 1 to 5 in a public school in a lower-middle-class neighborhood. The number of subjects at each grade level was about 20, which was always the entire class.

Using about 200 identical plastic chips, I told the children in individual interviews that I had hidden some chips under a folder and that I would show these chips to them for a very brief moment that would be too short for them to count the chips. I demonstrated 3 seconds of exposure with my hand and told the children that I wanted them to write an estimated number before counting the chips. First graders were shown 70 to 80 chips, and the older children were shown 98 to 120 chips. (The number varied from child to child to prevent the subjects from being informed by their classmates.) When the child had written the estimated number, I asked him or her to count the chips, to find out how close the estimate was. I then asked the child to close his or her eyes so that I could hide a few chips in my hand. To figure out how many chips I was hiding in my hand, I asked the child to count those remaining on the table, but to count them *by tens*.

The first request for a count was to observe how the children counted a large number of chips spontaneously. The second request for a count was to observe how they counted by tens.

All the first graders and most of the others counted the large quantity of chips spontaneously by ones. Spontaneously counting by tens, by separating the whole into heaps of 10, appeared for the first time in the fourth grade, among only 14% of the class. (I was so surprised by the extent of these children's preference for counting by ones that I sometimes asked fourth and fifth graders to count all 200 of my chips, to see if they might shift to counting by tens. They still counted by ones!)

Table 2.8 shows what happened when I asked the children to count by tens. This task revealed that counting by tens involves problems in making part-whole relationships. The lowest level of response, shown at the top of this table, called "No idea how," includes a large variety of behaviors ranging from saying, "I don't know how," to counting each chip by saying, "Ten, 20, 30," and so on.

The second category, called "Making heaps of 10, without conservation of the whole," is significant. When I asked first graders to count the chips by tens, they easily made heaps of 10, as they had been trained to do in class. However, these children did not go on to count anything after making groups of tens. I had to ask them how many there were all together, and these children counted the heaps and answered, "Seven." I exclaimed, "Seven chips all together? I see more than seven," strongly expressing disagreement. The first graders thereupon counted the chips in one heap and said, "Ten." It did not occur to me until later that these children could not think *simultaneously* about the heaps and the chips in the heaps. Since they could not think *simultaneously* about the tens and the ones, they continued to say that there were either 7 (heaps) or 10 (chips), but never 70, when I repeatedly asked them how many chips there were on the table all together. Only by counting by ones, like the level 2 children in Ross's (1986) study, could these first graders find 70 chips.

The third category, called "Not separating the whole into parts," was also surprising. The children in this category in reality counted by ones. They counted out 10 chips first and left them in a group. They then counted out 10 other chips, making a separate heap, but then said, "Twenty," as they joined the second heap to the first one. They then counted out another heap of 10, spatially separating them from the heap of 20. As they pushed this heap of 10 to combine it with the first 20 chips, these children said, "Thirty." They continued this process until they had counted all the chips.

The fourth category, "Making heaps of 10, with conservation of the whole," is the same as Ross's (1986) highest level. The children in this group made separate heaps of 10 and then counted the heaps afterward to determine the total number of chips. Unlike the children in the second category, those in the fourth category made heaps of 10 *with the intention of going back and counting the chips by tens.* In other words, the children in the fourth category could think about both the ones and the tens simultaneously. This is an indication of their having constructed a system of tens on the system of ones.

The third category becomes understandable in light of this evolutionary process. Children who have only the system of ones in their heads will temporarily make a heap of 10 chips to comply with the interviewer's request. However, they do not cut up the series of ones into segments of 10 because they cannot yet think in terms of tens.

It can be seen in Table 2.8 that the system of tens (level 4) appears for the first time in the second grade and that the proportion of children in this category increases thereafter. (The percentage decreases in Grade 4, but this is a problem of small samples.)

Although this study involved only 100 children, it is supported by the 60 years of research by Piaget and his collaborators that repeatedly demonstrated the appearance of concrete operations at age 7 to 8 (in second grade) in a host of cognitive tasks. The construction of part-whole rela-

TABLE 2.8: Four Ways of Responding When Asked to
Count by Tens (Percentage)

	Grade				
	1	2	3	4	5
	(n=21)	(n=18)	(n=21*)	(n=22)	(n=18)
1. No idea how	33	6			
2. Making heaps of 10 without conservation of the whole	29	0			
3. Not separating the whole into parts	38	56	19	64	22
4. Making heaps of 10 with conservation of the whole		39	71	36	78

*The behavior of 2 children (10%) did not fall into
any of the four categories.

tionships has been found at this age in classification (Inhelder & Piaget,
1959/1964), the measurement of length (Piaget, Inhelder, & Szeminska,
1948/1960), simple fractions (Piaget, Inhelder, & Szeminska, 1948/1960),
and commutativity of addition (Gréco, 1962).

With the preceding findings from research as a background, I would
now like to explain why traditional place-value instruction is off the mark
and why it is undesirable to teach the algorithm of double-column addition in the first two grades.

IMPLICATIONS FOR INSTRUCTION

Place-Value Instruction

Many first-grade teachers are now told to begin at the "concrete" level
of "counting real objects" and to ask children to make bundles of 10 straws
or toothpicks using rubber bands. When enough bundles have been
made, the teachers go on to exercises on tens and ones by posing questions such as, "How many tens do you have?" and, "How many ones do
you have?"

Similar exercises are then given at the next level, the "semiconcrete"
level of "counting objects in pictures." Instead of putting rubber bands
around objects, children are now instructed to draw circles around each

group of 10 objects printed on paper. They then fill in the blanks in exercises such as the following, which are intended to move them to the "symbolic" level:

_____ tens   _____ ones

There are many variations on these exercises; however, they are all similar in that they attempt to teach our conventional system of writing from outside the child. All of them overlook the necessity of the child's construction of the system of tens on the system of ones, through constructive abstraction.

The empirical knowledge the child can get from three bundles and two loose objects is presented schematically in Figure 2.4a. Completely missing from this figure are the mental relationships the child has to introduce among the objects to quantify them numerically. In Figure 2.4b, I have drawn circles, ovals, and lines to indicate the systems of ones and tens that the child has to impose on the objects. Each one of these systems, it will be recalled, consists of the synthesis of order and hierarchical inclu-

Figure 2.4.   Schematic representation of (a) empirical knowledge of groups of objects and (b) mental structure of tens and ones imposed on the objects.

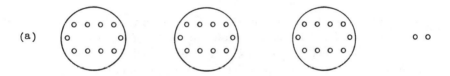

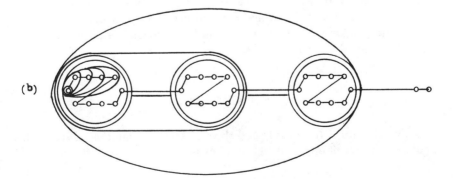

sion. In Figure 2.4b, the hierarchical inclusion of ones is drawn only up to five because the figure would otherwise have become too confusing.

Ross's (1986) research about children's conservation of 4 tens and 8 ones and my research about their counting of 70 to 120 chips should convince the reader that all this empirical counting and making of groups of 10 is off the mark, even with base-10 blocks. The system of tens has to be constructed by children, in their heads, on *their* system of ones, through constructive abstraction.

Double-Column Addition

All the math textbook series now introduce the rule, or algorithm, of double-column addition that makes children add the ones first and then the tens. The beauty of this rule is that it allows us to treat every column as ones. This procedure is efficient for adults who understand place value. For first and second graders who do not understand it yet, however, this algorithm has the effect of confusing them and "unteaching" what little they understand of place value.

Take, for example, a problem such as the following:

$$13$$
$$+13$$

Traditionally instructed children will say,"Three and 3 is 6, so I put a 6 down here. And 1 and 1 is 2, so I put a 2 down, and the answer is 26." In other words, for them $3 + 3$ and $1 + 1$ together make 26, rather than 8! It is little wonder that they cope with instruction by memorizing rules. Memorizing is the only way to cope with something that does not make sense.

We will see in Chapter 6 that when children are allowed to invent their own procedures, they invariably add the tens first and then the ones. The mental procedure they usually invent for the preceding problem is stated as follows: "Ten and 10 is 20, and 3 and 3 is 6, so the answer is 26." By talking and thinking about the 1 of 13 as 10, children are encouraged to figure out how place value "works."

CONCLUSION

In this chapter, I have explained through the presentation of research findings why traditional instruction is in need of change in the areas of place value and double-column addition. In Chapter 5, new objectives in this area are presented, and in Chapter 6 better ways of teaching are described. Comparisons of results of new and old ways of teaching can be found in Chapter 10.

CHAPTER 3

The Importance of
Social Interaction

Educators often say that peer interaction is important because children learn from each other. I agree that children learn many things from each other, but this is not my reason for advocating social interaction among peers.

Logico-mathematical knowledge has its source inside each child and is elaborated through each child's own mental action. In the logico-mathematical realm, therefore, other people are not the sources of knowledge for the child to internalize. Rather, other people's ideas are important because they provide occasions for children to think critically about their own ideas in relation to other people's. For example, if one child says that $5 + 4 = 8$, and another says that $5 + 4 = 9$, this disagreement leads to critical thinking by both children, through the exchange of viewpoints. Logico-mathematical knowledge is not acquired by internalization from someone else but by each child's own autonomous thinking. When children are convinced that someone else's idea makes better sense than theirs, they change their minds and correct themselves, from the inside.

Piaget (1980) attributed great importance to social interaction. To him, such exchanges were indispensable, both for children's elaboration of logical thought and for adults' construction of sciences. As he put it,

> Certain educators say sometimes that my theory is only "cognitive," and that I neglected the importance of social aspects of the child's development. It is true that most of my publications have dealt with various aspects of cognitive development, particularly the development of operativity, but in my first works I emphasized the importance of interindividual exchanges sufficiently not to feel the need afterwards to return to it. In fact, it is clear that the confrontation of points of view is already indispensable in childhood for the elaboration of logical thought, and such confrontations become increasingly more important in the elaboration of sciences by adults. Without the diversity of theories and the constant search for going beyond the contradictions among them, scientific progress would not have been possible. [p. vii]

Piaget did not experimentally verify his theory about the importance of social interaction, but other researchers at the University of Geneva did. I have selected a series of studies by Doise and Mugny (1984) as an example. They demonstrate that even a 10-minute discussion by two people whose ideas are both wrong at the same level can result in the construction of higher-level thinking.

EXCHANGE BETWEEN CHILD AND ADULT

Experimental Conditions

Doise and Mugny (1984) selected a task involving the conservation of length, for their series of studies. Two rails 4 cm wide and 22 cm long were used in the experimental session in which social interaction took place. Some toy wagons were also available at the beginning of the experiment, so that the child could play with the material and understand the meaning of the rails.

The two rails were then placed in visual correspondence, and the child judged them to be of equal length (see Figure 3.1a). One of the rails was then pushed slightly to the right, as shown in Figure 3.1b, and the child was asked if the rails had the same length or if one was longer than the other. Since all the children included in this study were nonconservers, with a mean age of 6 years and 3 months, they all said at this point that one rail was longer than the other. When asked to justify their answer, the children explained that one of the rails was longer because it stuck out beyond the other one. This is a typical response. Nonconservers think

Figure 3.1.　Successive configurations in the conservation-of-equal-length task.

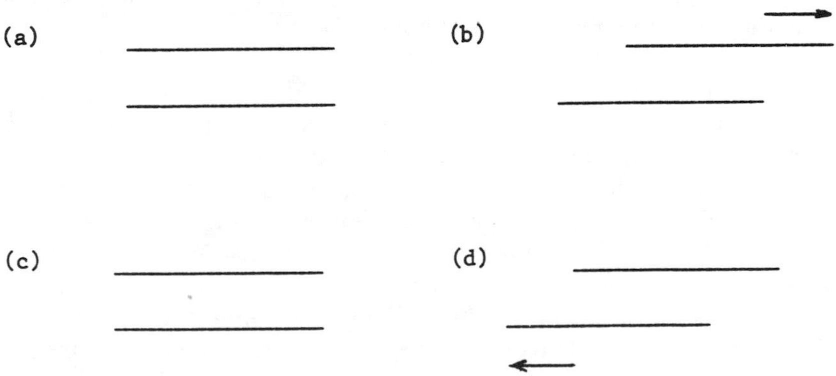

only about the uneven unaligned ends of the rails, and base their judgments on the fact that one rail sticks out beyond the other.

Doise and Mugny (1984) ideally wanted to conduct this experiment with pairs of children who would disagree in their judgments in certain ways. More specifically, they wanted to compare the outcomes of the following three conditions:

1. *Incorrect answer.* The nonconserver would exchange points of view with someone who disagreed but had a wrong answer at the same cognitive level. For example, if the nonconserving subject said the top rail was longer in Figure 3.1b, this condition required a stooge who would say, "I think the bottom rail is longer because it sticks out right here (on the opposite side)." The stooge's answer would always be the opposite of the subject's, and the two answers would be equally wrong, at the same cognitive level. The experimenter would then ask the subject and the stooge to come to an agreement.
2. *Correct answer.* The nonconserver would exchange points of view with someone who disagreed and stated the correct answer. The stooge in this condition would say, "I think the two rails have the same length because the top rail sticks out on this side but the bottom rail sticks out on the other side. That's why I think the two rails have the same length." The experimenter would then encourage the subject and stooge to talk to each other and consider each other's point of view. (Unlike in the previous condition, the stooge's idea here would be at a higher cognitive level than the child's.)
3. *Control.* The nonconserver would not exchange points of view in this condition and would work alone with the experimenter. The questions put to him or her would be the same as in the other two conditions, but the number of items would be doubled to fill up the same amount of time as in the other two conditions.

Since it was impossible to expect a 6-year-old to act as a stooge, Doise and Mugny (1984) decided to use an adult for this experiment. In each session, therefore, there were two adults and a child. The experimenter asked the child if the two unaligned rails had the same length or not, and when the child said that one was longer than the other, the experimenter turned to the other adult (the stooge) and asked what he or she thought. The stooge in the first condition always gave the equally incorrect but opposite answer to that of the child. The experimenter then pointed out that there was a disagreement and asked if the two individuals could try to come to an agreement. The stooge in the second condition, by contrast, gave the correct answer.

The stooge responded differently to the different statements the subject made. For example, if the subject in the first experimental condition adopted the stooge's incorrect answer, which was often the case, the stooge then shifted to the child's initial response by saying, "But I agree with you that this one is longer," pointing to the rail initially chosen by the child. "It sticks out here." If, on the other hand, the child in this same condition switched and gave the correct answer of equal length, the two adults avoided showing any sign of approval and repeated the wrong answer. When the child persisted in giving the correct answer, the experimenter decided to go on to the second item or to stop the experiment without spending 5 minutes per item, as originally planned.

Pretest, First Posttest, and Second Posttest

The pretest, first posttest, and second posttest activities all consisted of two conservation tasks that were individually administered. One involved rods of equal length and the other one involved chains of unequal length. These tasks were given as follows.

Conservation of Equal Lengths. The child was shown two wooden rods of the same color, each 10 cm long. "These are sticks, but let's pretend they are roads," the experimenter said (Doise & Mugny, 1984). As she placed the sticks in visual correspondence (see Figure 3.1a), she ran her finger along one rod and asked, "Do you think here you'd have to walk as much as on the other road?" running her finger along the other stick. If the child did not understand the question, the experimenter repeated it with reference to an ant: "Do you think an ant would have to walk as much here as here? Or do you think it would have a longer way to go on one of the roads?" The child was then asked about length: "Do you think the sticks both have the same length? Or do you think there is one that is longer than the other?" (All these questions were carefully asked because young children often say that the roads are the same but not the lengths. For many young children, length refers to the point of arrival of the rod, and not to the distance from the point of departure to the point of arrival.)

The same kinds of questions were posed with all four of the configurations shown in Figure 3.1. In (a) the two rods are in visual correspondence. In (b) one rod has been pushed to the right. The rod is returned to its original position in (c), and the other rod has been pushed to the left in (d).

The children were categorized into three groups after the pretest, first posttest, and second posttest: nonconservers, intermediates, and conservers. The nonconservers said that the roads had the same length in the situations illustrated by (a) and (c) in Figure 3.1; but, when a rod was moved as shown in (b) and (d), they said that one was longer than the other. Usually but not always, they said that the one that had been pushed in either direction was longer and explained that it stuck out beyond the one that had not been pushed.

Conservers, on the other hand, judged the two rods as having the same length in all four of the situations shown in Figure 3.1. When asked to justify their answers, they confidently gave arguments such as, "All you did was to move one, and we can put it back the way it was before" or, "This rod sticks out on this end, but the other rod sticks out on the other end; so the length is the same" (Doise & Mugny, 1984).

Children classified as intermediates were in transition. Some gave correct answers but could not justify them. Some gave the correct answer on one item but not on the other. Others vacillated and kept changing their minds.

Conservation of Unequal Lengths. Two chains were used in this task, a 10-cm chain and a 15-cm chain. They were presented in the configurations shown in Figure 3.2, and similar questions were posed about their relative lengths as were asked about the rods previously.

Nonconservers said in situation (b) that the two chains had the same length, and that the ant would walk as much on one road as on the other. Their justification for making this statement was that the extremities of the roads coincided. In situation (d), these nonconservers said that the bottom road was longer because it stuck out beyond the other. Noncon-

Figure 3.2. Successive configurations in the conservation-of-unequal-length task.

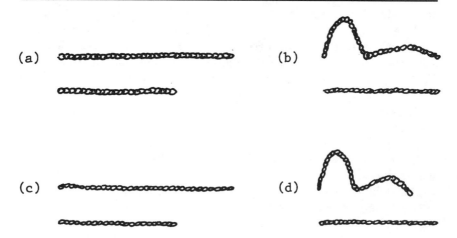

(a)

(b)

(c)

(d)

servers maintained this response, even when they were reminded of their previous statement that the top road was longer.

Conservers, on the other hand, confidently judged the 15-cm chain to be longer in all the situations shown in Figure 3.2. They could also explain the logical necessity of their judgments.

The intermediates usually said that the 15-cm chain was longer in situation (b) but not in situation (d). They also had trouble justifying their correct answers. In addition, their responses were characterized by hesitation and vacillation.

Procedure

As stated earlier, the children who were included in this study were all nonconservers on the pretest. Those who were either conservers or intermediates on the pretest were excluded from the study.

The children who were found to be nonconservers on the pretest were randomly assigned to the three experimental conditions described earlier: (1) exchanging points of view with an adult who gave an incorrect answer at the same cognitive level, (2) exchanging points of view with an adult who gave the correct answer, and (3) not exchanging points of view but spending the same amount of time thinking about the same questions (control condition). The first posttest was given individually, immediately after the experimental session was finished. A second posttest was given 10 days later to evaluate the stability of the gains.

Results

By comparing the results of the children who were nonconservers on the pretest with their results on the two posttests, we can demonstrate the progress that was or was not made by them. The data are presented in Table 3.1.

The first point to be made is that the nonconservers who exchanged points of view with an adult made considerably more progress than those in the control group who were exposed only to the material and questions. All 13 of the children in the control group remained nonconservers on the conservation-of-equal-length task at the first posttest, and 12 of the 13 remained nonconservers on the conservation-of-unequal-length task. On the second posttest, these figures had changed very little, to 12 and 10, respectively. By contrast, at least half of those in the two other groups made progress by moving up to being intermediates or conservers.

It may not be surprising to find out that the children who were exposed

TABLE 3.1: Results of Nonconservers' Exchanges
of Viewpoints with an Adult

	Equal Length			Unequal Length		
	Noncons.	Interm.	Cons.	Noncons.	Interm.	Cons.
First posttest						
Incorrect answer (n=20)	11	1	8	7	5	8
Correct answer (n=19)	1	2	16	10	5	4
Control (n=13)	13	0	0	12	1	0
Second posttest						
Incorrect answer (n=20)	11	2	7	5	8	7
Correct answer (n=19)	2	4	13	8	6	5
Control (n=13)	12	1	0	10	2	1

Adapted from Doise, W., & Mugny, G. (1984). The Social Development
of the Intellect. New York: Pergamon, pp. 86–87.

to the correct answer made progress. The surprising and significant finding of this study is that exchanging points of view with an adult who gave
an incorrect answer at the same cognitive level was beneficial. If we take
the conservation-of-unequal-length task as the more stringent "transfer"
test, we can see from Table 3.1 that, at the first posttest, the children who
were confronted with an incorrect answer (at the same cognitive level)
made slightly more gains, proportionately, than those who were confronted with the correct answer. By the second posttest, even more children had made gains, with the incorrect-answer group still in the lead.

Many questions can be raised about the relative desirability of con-
fronting the child with a correct or incorrect answer. I will not enter into
the details of this question and will focus instead on Piaget's theory, constructivism, as it compares to the transmission-and-internalization theory
of math education. If children acquired logico-mathematical knowledge
by internalization from the environment, the subjects in the incorrect-
answer group would not have made progress on either of these conservation tasks. Their progress can be explained only by constructivism.
These children were confronted with an answer that contradicted theirs
but was at the same cognitive level. When they tried to reconcile the
contradiction, they coordinated the opposing viewpoints and constructed
a higher-level relationship that included the opposing viewpoints.

The gains of the correct-answer group are also interesting in this regard. The gains this group made on both conservation tasks can be explained by constructivism. While it is possible to explain the gains of this group on the equal-length task using the transmission-and-internalization theory, this is not true of their progress on the unequal-length task. The correct answer may have helped these children on the equal-length task by challenging them with a *different* point of view. As a result, many of these children may have autonomously constructed a higher-level relationship rather than merely mimicking the adult. Those who mimicked the right answer on the first posttest appear to have forgotten it on the second posttest. The results for this group on the unequal-lengths task (the "transfer" test) suggested gains on the second posttest while those for the equal-length task demonstrated some losses.

EXCHANGE BETWEEN PAIRS OF CHILDREN

The preceding experiment was one of four in a series by Doise and Mugny (1984). I would like to describe one more of the four because it is very similar to the preceding experiment but concerns the exchange of points of view between pairs of children, rather than between an adult and a child.

Experimental Conditions

There were two conditions in this experiment. In the first, the control condition, the children were individually questioned in a way similar to the previous experiment. In the second condition, the children were interviewed in pairs. The two children sat face to face across a table and were asked to exchange points of view and to come to an agreement if they disagreed. If, throughout the experiment, there was no evidence of disagreement on an audiotape, those children were assigned to the category called "without conflict" (see Table 3.2). If there was recorded evidence of disagreement at some point during the experiment, those children were assigned to the category called "with conflict" (see Table 3.2).

Procedure

As in the previous study, all the children who participated were those who were found to be nonconservers on the pretest. The tasks used in the pretest, first posttest, and second posttest were the same as in the experiment with an adult stooge.

TABLE 3.2:   Results of Exchanges of Viewpoints
Among Pairs of Nonconserving Children

	Equal Length			Unequal Length		
	Noncons.	Interm.	Cons.	Noncons.	Interm.	Cons.
Posttest						
Individual controls (n̲=12)	11	0	1	11	1	0
Pairs without conflict (n̲=18)	14	3	1	12	6	0
Pairs with conflict (n=18)	7	10	1	7	10	1

Adapted from Doise, W., & Mugny, G. (1984). The Social Development
of the Intellect. New York: Pergamon, p. 94.

Results

As can be seen in Table 3.2, of the children in the control group, who
were individually questioned about the lengths of the rails, only one
made any progress. The group that made the most progress consisted of
pairs who disagreed and exchanged ideas in an attempt to come to an
agreement. Eleven out of the 18 children in pairs with conflict made
progress, both on the equal-length and unequal-length tasks. By contrast,
only four and six children, respectively, in pairs without conflict made
progress on the equal-length and unequal-length task. Doise and Mugny
(1984) report that these gains were very stable on the second posttest.

The authors speculate about the modest gains made by the pairs of
children who did not disagree, as far as they could determine from the
audiotape. Their hypothesis is that the children who did not verbally
challenge each other may nevertheless have exchanged viewpoints in
nonverbal ways.

CONCLUSION

The experimental studies cited in this chapter are too small to be de-
finitive. The importance of social interaction, however, can be gleaned in
light of the many other experiments reported by Doise and Mugny, as
well as by Perret-Clermont (1980), and the many volumes by Piaget and
his collaborators documenting constructivism in detail. The evidence
supporting Piaget's constructivism is voluminous, and the works most relevant to primary mathematics are Piaget (1937/1954, 1946/1971), Piaget

and Szeminska (1941/1965), Piaget and Inhelder (1948/1967), Piaget, Inhelder, and Szeminska (1948/1960), and Inhelder and Piaget (1959/1964).

Evidence of constructivism can also be found in the long history of
mathematics and the physical sciences. If adults construct mathematic
and scientific knowledge by debating points of conflict, children, too, can
be expected to construct logico-mathematical knowledge by the same
process.

The importance of social interaction is discussed further in the next
chapter, which concerns autonomy as the broad, long-term goal of education. The history of mathematics and the sciences attests to the intellectual autonomy of the human species. Human beings construct knowledge by trying to make ever better sense of their experiences. They are
not passive vessels who can only hold the knowledge that is poured into
their heads.

Part II

GOALS AND OBJECTIVES

CHAPTER 4

Autonomy: The Goal of Education for Piaget

In traditional mathematics education, goals and objectives are conceptualized in terms of a scope-and-sequence chart. Typically, this conceptualization begins with headings such as the following, which are found in the Level 2 teacher's guide from the Mathematics Today Series (Abbott & Wells, 1985):

Numbers and numeration
Addition of whole numbers
Subtraction of whole numbers
Multiplication of whole numbers
Division of whole numbers
Fractions
Measurement, time, and money
Geometry
Graphing, probability, statistics
Problem solving

In an effort to update and improve mathematics education throughout the country, the National Council of Teachers of Mathematics (NCTM) is publishing a document entitled *Curriculum and Evaluation Standards for School Mathematics*. Discussion and quotations from this document, in this and the next chapter, are based on the July 1988 draft. The goals for students in grades K–12 delineated in this document are much broader than the traditional ones in the foregoing list. They consist of the following:

That they learn to value mathematics
That they become confident in their ability to do mathematics
That they become mathematical problem solvers
That they learn to communicate mathematically
That they learn to reason mathematically

These broader goals are superior to those of traditional math textbooks because, first of all, they focus on the learner rather than only on successive specific aspects of mathematics. The authors of the NCTM document should also be commended for recognizing children's confidence as a major goal.

From the standpoint of a Piagetian educator who advocates autonomy as the aim of education, however, the NCTM goals still seem too narrow. The word *mathematics* appears in every one of the five goals, and I wanted to delete it from "that they learn to reason mathematically." I also wanted to change "that they become confident in their ability to do mathematics" to "that they become confident in their ability to think." As for "that they learn to communicate mathematically," I wanted to change this statement to "that they learn to exchange viewpoints with other people."

I also wondered whether or not the authors of the NCTM document thought about children's social and moral development. In this chapter, I review what Piaget meant by autonomy in general and as the goal of education, and explain why constructivist arithmetic education would not be constructivist outside the context of autonomy as the broad, long-range goal. I also argue that teachers foster or hinder children's social and moral development, whether or not they intend to do so, as they teach every subject.

WHAT IS AUTONOMY, AND HOW DOES IT DEVELOP?

Autonomy means being governed by oneself. It is the opposite of heteronomy, which means being governed by somebody else. Autonomy in Piaget's theory is not the political *right* to make decisions but the *ability* to make decisions by taking relevant factors into account, independently of rewards and punishment. Autonomy has a moral and an intellectual aspect, and I first clarify what Piaget meant by moral autonomy.

Moral Autonomy

An extreme example of moral autonomy is Martin Luther King's struggle for civil rights. By taking relevant factors into account such as the welfare of all citizens, King became convinced that the laws discriminating against blacks were immoral. He thus systematically challenged the discriminatory laws in spite of the threats of assassination, police brutality, arrest, jails, dogs, and water hoses that awaited him. A morally autonomous person is governed by what he or she believes to be right, and not by the reward system.

An extreme example of moral heteronomy is the Watergate coverup affair. The men under President Nixon were governed by him and went along with what they knew to be wrong, reaping the rewards the president dispensed to those who helped him in the coverup attempt.

In *The Moral Judgment of the Child,* Piaget (1932/1965) gave more commonplace examples of autonomy and heteronomy. He interviewed children between the ages of 6 and 14 and asked them, for example, why it was bad to tell lies. Young, heteronomous children replied, "Because you get punished when you tell lies." "Would it be OK to tell lies if you were not punished for them?" Piaget asked, and young children answered, "Yes." He went on to inquire, "Which is worse, telling a lie to an adult or to another child?" Young, heteronomous children responded that it was worse to lie to an adult. Why? "Because adults can tell when something is not true." Older, more autonomous children, on the other hand, tended to say that it was sometimes necessary to lie to adults, but that it was rotten to do it to another child.

The important question for parents and teachers to ask is, What causes certain children to become more autonomous than others? Piaget's answer to this question is that adults reinforce children's natural heteronomy when they use rewards and punishment, thereby hindering the development of autonomy. By refraining from using rewards and punishment, and by exchanging points of view with children instead, we can foster the development of autonomy, he said.

For example, if a child tells a lie, an adult can punish the child by depriving him or her of dessert. But the adult can also look the child straight in the eye with affection and skepticism and say instead, "I *really* can't believe what you are saying because—" (and give the reason). "And when you tell me something next time, I am not sure I'll be able to believe you, because I think you lied this time. I want you to go to your room and think about what happened."

Children who are raised with this kind of exchange of viewpoints are likely, over time, to construct from within the value of honesty. Children who are confronted with the fact that other people cannot believe them are likely, over time, to come to the conclusion that it is better in the long run for people to be able to trust each other.

An essential element here is a warm human relationship of mutual respect and affection between the child and the adult. If children believe that an adult does not care about them anyway, they will have no reason to want to be believed.

In general, punishment leads to three possible outcomes. The first one is calculation of risks. Children who are punished will learn to calculate their chances of getting caught the next time and the price they might have to pay if they are caught. While these calculations may be good for children's learning about probability, their value for children's moral development is obviously questionable.

The second possible outcome of punishment is the opposite of the first one, namely, blind obedience. In our culture especially, sensitive little girls will do anything to avoid being punished, and this is how they give the impression that punishment works. When children become blindly obedient, they come to feel psychologically safe because they become respectable and do not have to make decisions any more. Rather than thinking about relevant factors, all these children have to do is to obey.

The third common outcome of punishment is a derivative of the second, namely, revolt. Many "good," model children surprise us eventually by beginning to cut classes, take drugs, and engage in other acts that characterize delinquency. Their reason for switching to these behaviors is that they are tired of living for their parents and teachers, and think the time has come for them to start living for themselves. While acts of revolt may look like autonomous acts, there is a vast difference between autonomy and revolt. In a revolt, the child figures out what is expected and deliberately does the opposite. A child who always has to go counter to the norm is not autonomous.

Many behaviorists and others believe that punishment is bad because it is negative, but that rewards are positive and good. However, rewards do not make children any more autonomous than punishment. The child who fills out a work sheet only to get a sticker and the one who does chores only to get money are governed by others just as much as the child who is "good" only to avoid being punished. The Watergate affair happened because the men under the president expected to be rewarded by him.

When adults exchange viewpoints with children, this fosters the development of autonomy by enabling children to consider various perspectives. When children can take relevant factors into account, such as other people's rights and feelings, they construct from within the rule, for example, that it is better for human beings to deal honestly with each other. A person who has constructed this conviction cannot lie in situations like the Watergate affair, no matter what reward is offered.[1]

Intellectual Autonomy

In the intellectual realm, too, autonomy means being governed by oneself by being able to take relevant factors into account, and heteronomy

---

[1]The reader interested in knowing more about rewards, punishments, and sanctions by reciprocity is referred to *Young Children Reinvent Arithmetic* (Kamii, 1985, pp. 40–45).

means being governed by somebody else. An extreme example of intellectual autonomy is Copernicus, who promulgated the heliocentric theory in 1543, when everybody else believed that the sun revolved around the earth. The scientists of his time laughed at him and did not even let him finish his lectures. Copernicus, however, was autonomous enough to remain convinced of the truth of his theory.

An intellectually heteronomous person, by contrast, uncritically believes what he is told, including illogical conclusions, propaganda, and slogans.

In the intellectual realm, too, what reinforces children's natural heteronomy, thereby hindering the development of autonomy, is the system of rewards and punishment. What fosters the development of autonomy in the intellectual realm, too, is the exchange of points of view.

Unfortunately, in math education, children are taught in ways that reinforce their heteronomy. For example, if a first grader writes the number 8 under the problem shown below, most teachers mark this answer as being wrong. If, on the other hand, a first grader writes 26 under this problem, most teachers will give some sort of reward.

$$\begin{array}{r} 13 \\ + 13 \\ \hline \end{array}$$

As was pointed out in Chapter 2, first graders do not understand place value and think that the 1 in 13 means one. If they write the correct answer, therefore, they do not understand why this answer is correct. For them, this problem is two separate problems: $3 + 3$ and $1 + 1$. They follow the rule of writing two answers vertically in the designated spots, and of reading the numbers horizontally to make one answer out of two.

For the reader who is skeptical about the preceding argument, I give another example about division. I suggest that the reader ask any fourth grader why he or she begins on the left-hand side in the following computation, instead of beginning on the right-hand side as in adding, subtracting, or multiplying multidigit numbers.

$$\begin{array}{r} 2 \\ 4 \overline{)938} \end{array}$$

The fourth grader's answer is likely to be, "I don't know why, but the teacher told me to do it like this." This is an example of intellectual heteronomy. Blindly following rules to get "right" answers reinforces young children's natural heteronomy and hinders the development of autonomy.

To return to the addition problem given earlier, it would be much better for the teacher to encourage the exchange of viewpoints among children than to reinforce "right" answers or to correct "wrong" ones. A way to encourage the exchange of viewpoints is to ask the class, "Does everybody agree?" In this situation, the children who got the right answer could not convince the others merely by saying, "The teacher said to do it this way." Those who got incorrect answers will correct themselves if and when they become convinced that another answer makes better sense. In the logico-mathematical realm, children are bound to arrive at the truth autonomously if they debate long enough.

AUTONOMY AS THE GOAL OF EDUCATION

The reader may have concluded by now that autonomy as the goal of education is a necessary consequence of constructivism. Once we understand the difference between the morality of autonomy and the morality of heteronomy, we become convinced of the desirability of the former. Once we understand the superiority of intellectual autonomy, likewise, we become convinced of the desirability of independent, honest, and critical thinking rather than the recitation of "right" answers.

Figure 4.1 shows the relationship between autonomy as the goal of education and the actual goals of most educators and the public today. I wanted to put the label "Heteronomy" on the circle to the right but did not because most educators today do not *intentionally* try to foster heteronomy in their students.

In the shaded part of the circle, which represents these misdirected goals, belong all the words we memorized in school just to pass one test

Figure 4.1.   Autonomy as the aim of education, in relation to the goals of most educators today.

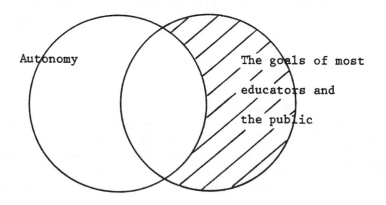

after another. We all remember the joy of being free to forget the words we crammed into our heads just for exams. Most of us were conformists, governed by grades. Included in the shaded part of Figure 4.1 are also the rules, or algorithms, we followed blindly in math to get "right" answers. As I pointed out in *Young Children Reinvent Arithmetic* (Kamii, 1985), kindergarten children do not grab their erasers when we ask them how they got an answer. In first grade, by contrast, if we select a correct answer on a work sheet a child is filling out and ask, "How did you get this answer?" the child often starts erasing the answer. This is a symptom of heteronomy. This child has learned to distrust his or her own thinking and to be governed by someone else's thinking.

In the circle labeled "Autonomy" I include both moral and intellectual autonomy. It is significant to note that in his discussion of autonomy as the goal of education, Piaget (1948/1973) selected math education to use as an example in pointing out that children's social, moral, and intellectual development are inseparable in the reality of a classroom.

Piaget's (1948/1973) argument began with the statement that all children must do their own thinking autonomously to construct logico-mathematical knowledge. In the logico-mathematical realm, there is no substitute for each child's own thinking, because this knowledge has to be constructed from within. Piaget went on to point out that children's thinking develops in a social context. Every classroom has a social climate, and this climate cannot encourage the free exchange of viewpoints in the intellectual realm while stifling it in the moral realm. If children are silenced in the social and moral realm, they will not feel free to express their ideas in the intellectual realm, either.

Going back to Figure 4.1, the overlap between the two circles stands for the little bit of autonomy we developed in spite of traditional, authoritarian schooling. Our ability to read, write, and do some math are examples of the things we learned in school that we did not forget after the examinations. Other examples of things that belong to this intersection are ability to put events in historical context, to read maps and charts, and to understand a few things scientifically.

Within the larger circle of autonomy, I conceptualize social, moral, attitudinal, and cognitive development hierarchically, as shown in Figure 4.2. Social and moral goals are conceptualized before cognitive goals, because cognitive development takes place in a social context. For example, a discussion or game cannot take place in a classroom where children are constantly bickering or trying to avoid the teacher's control.

The social and moral goals as a whole aim at reducing the teacher's power as much as possible and at fostering self-government (democracy). When children are allowed to make decisions, they often make the same

Figure 4.2.   The hierarchical conceptualization of goals in the context of autonomy as the broad aim of education.

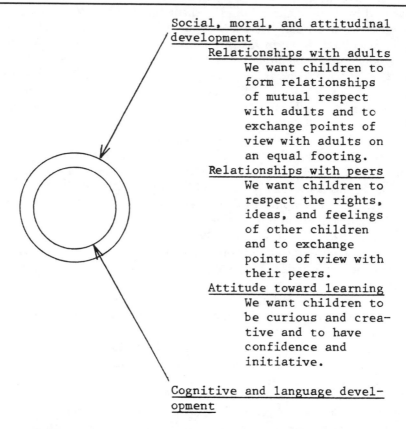

Social, moral, and attitudinal
development
    Relationships with adults
        We want children to
        form relationships
        of mutual respect
        with adults and to
        exchange points of
        view with adults on
        an equal footing.
    Relationships with peers
        We want children to
        respect the rights,
        ideas, and feelings
        of other children
        and to exchange
        points of view with
        their peers.
    Attitude toward learning
        We want children to
        be curious and crea-
        tive and to have
        confidence and
        initiative.
Cognitive and language development

rules that adults would make; however, they respect the rules that they
themselves make much more than the same rules imposed by adults.

Cognitive goals are conceptualized within attitudinal goals because at-
titudes heavily influence learning. For example, second graders who are
confident, creative, and full of initiative tackle a math problem such as
46 × 18 with gusto, as can be seen in Chapter 6. Traditionally instructed
second graders, by contrast, often say that they cannot solve such a problem because they have not been taught how.

The cognitive goals are not elaborated further here because they are
discussed in the next chapter on objectives for second-grade arithmetic.

I hope the reader can see that teachers may think they are teaching
only math during the math hour, but they are in reality fostering or hindering the development of autonomy as well. Traditional education im-

poses ready-made knowledge (such as algorithms) and ready-made moral rules and values as well. Constructivism suggests the desirability of not imposing these in prefabricated form. By encouraging children to construct their own knowledge and moral values, we can help them go much farther than "right" answers and "good" behaviors.

CHAPTER 5

Objectives for Second-Grade Arithmetic

The definition of goals and objectives is the most important part of education, because our goals determine *what* we teach and *how.* To the extent that our aims are shortsighted, contradictory, or based on incorrect assumptions, our efforts in the classroom become questionable.

Generally, authors of traditional math textbooks do not define objectives on the basis of research on children's cognitive development. They base their objectives on traditional assumptions about the nature of school mathematics and how children learn it. As already stated in the previous chapter, the National Council of Teachers of Mathematics (NCTM) is coming out with very different goals derived from a broader vision of school mathematics and research. I begin by discussing these two approaches to the definition of objectives and then present mine.

TRADITIONAL TEXTBOOK APPROACH

With respect to objectives in arithmetic, traditional textbooks can be said to have three characteristics. The first one is that the topics generally appear at an early grade and reappear over and over for review in later grades. The second characteristic is that the objectives aim at teaching techniques to children that will enable them to *write* correct answers in correct conventional forms. The third characteristic is that only one specific technique is presented at a time, and it is accompanied by numerous exercises of the same type designed for mastery of that technique. I will elaborate on each one of these characteristics in turn.

Early Introduction Followed by Repeated Review

I have already pointed out in Chapter 2 that place value is now introduced in first grade and reviewed in every subsequent grade of elementary school. It is not surprising, then, that two-digit addition and subtraction, with one "renaming" or "regrouping," are introduced in second grade and reviewed in every subsequent grade of elementary school. I believe there is something very wrong when the same topics have to be reviewed so many times every single year.

In the preceding paragraph, I put quotation marks around *renaming* and *regrouping* because these terms reflect misunderstanding of tens and ones. "One ten" is not another *name* for "10 ones." As can be seen in Figure 2.3 (p. 23), "10 ones" belongs to the system of ones, while "1 ten" belongs to the system of tens, which is built on the system of ones, by constructive abstraction. "One ten" is likewise not a concrete *group* of ones that can be regrouped; rather, it is an *idea* at a higher level of abstraction than the *idea* of ones.

To determine the proportion of pages in textbooks devoted to new contents at each grade level, Flanders (1987) analyzed three widely used series, namely, Addison-Wesley Mathematics (published by Addison-Wesley), Mathematics Today (published by Harcourt Brace Jovanovich), and Invitation to Mathematics (published by Scott, Foresman). By classifying each page of each textbook as new, old, or neutral, Flanders determined the percentages of pages devoted to new contents at each grade level. As can be seen in Figure 5.1, all three series consisted of a great

Figure 5.1.   Percentage of pages devoted to new content in three mathematics text series.

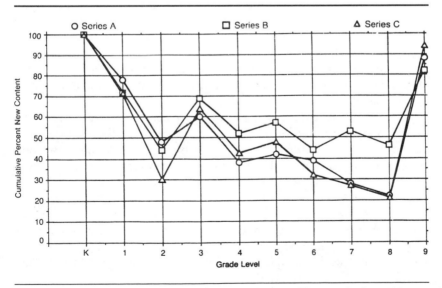

deal of review in grades 2 through 8. At the second-grade level, more than half of the pages were found to be used for review of what was presented in kindergarten or first grade. At the third-, fourth-, fifth-, and sixth-grade levels, the percentages of pages devoted to review were about 30–40, 50–60, 40–60, and 55–70, respectively.

Repeated review can thus be said to be a general characteristic of elementary math education. This would seem to me to point to the desirability of delaying the introduction of most topics until children can learn them easily and permanently.

Teaching Children to Write Correct Answers

The authors of traditional math series obviously do not set out to teach children only to become able to *write* correct answers. In reality, however, I have found that that is what they do, because of the approach they select.

For example, *Invitation to Mathematics: 1* (Bolster et al., 1987a), which is a first-grade text, introduces two-digit addition by presenting the "place-value box" illustrated in Figure 5.2a. Note that, in this situation, it makes no difference whether the child adds the ones first or the tens. However, the child is instructed to follow blindly the rule of adding the ones first, because the educator has future plans for two-digit addition involving "renaming" or "regrouping." First graders can easily learn to *write* correct answers to this kind of problem, but, as explained in Chapter 2, they think that the 1 in 13 means one and that the 2 in 24 means two. They thus succeed in writing correct answers without knowing why they have to start on the right-hand side or why 3 + 4 and 1 + 2 together make 37!

After 10 similar exercises, all using the place-value box, children are given 16 similar exercises on another page, without these boxes. First graders can thus continue to treat each two-digit problem as two one-digit problems. As long as they *write* correct answers in the correct spots, the teacher can maintain the illusion that the children are adding two-digit numbers.

On the following page of *Invitation to Mathematics: 1* (Bolster et al., 1987a), children are given the horizontal form, 23 + 33, with a grid, as shown in Figure 5.2b. Instead of encouraging children to add the numbers by thinking about them, the book tells them what to write and where.

In second grade, *Invitation to Mathematics: 2* (Bolster et al., 1987b) gives the more elaborate place-value box shown in Figure 5.2c. These are all attempts to use spatial relationships to teach children how to *write*

Figure 5.2. Place-value boxes presented in first and second grades for two-digit addition.

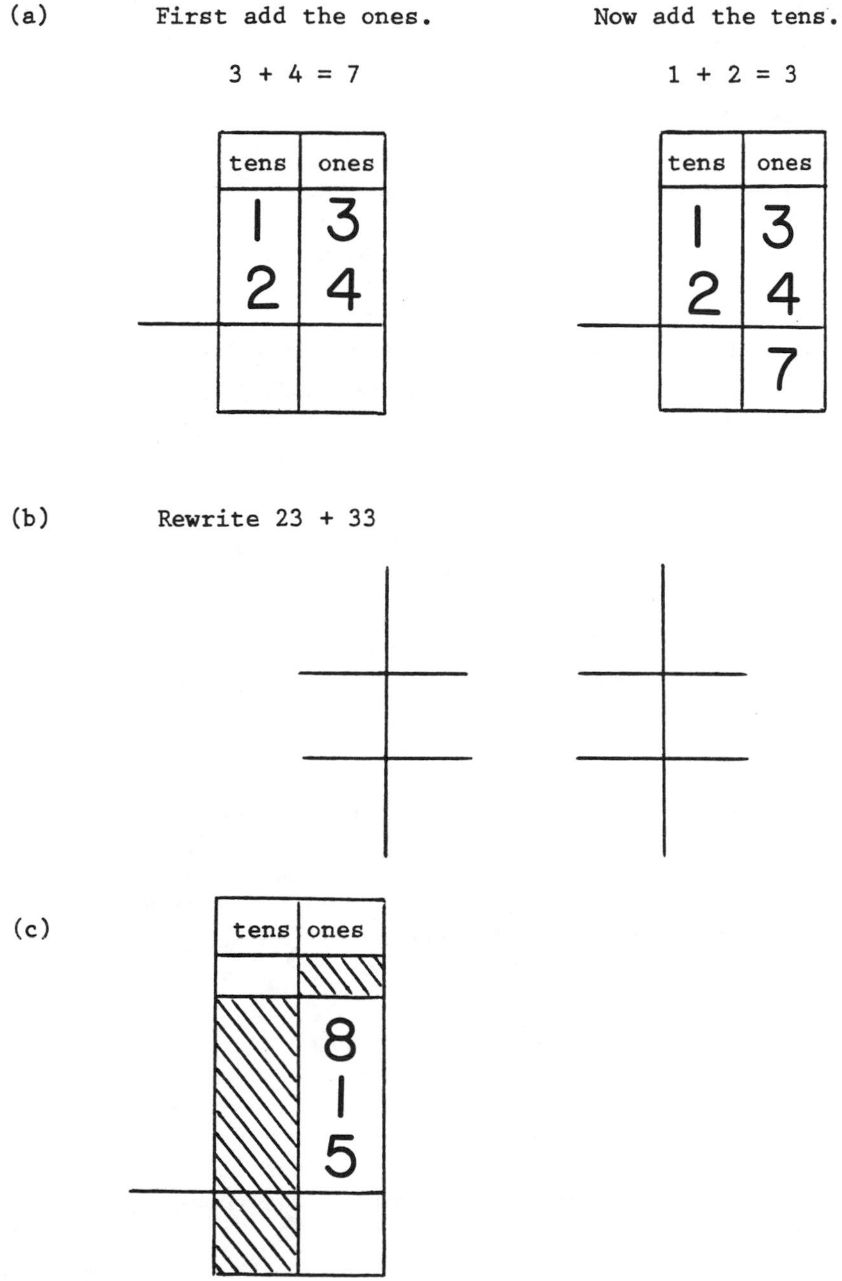

(a) First add the ones.   Now add the tens.

$$3 + 4 = 7$$ $$1 + 2 = 3$$

tens	ones
1	3
2	4

tens	ones
1	3
2	4
	7

(b) Rewrite 23 + 33

(c)

tens	ones
8	
1	
5	

(a) & (b) from Bolster et al. 1987a, (pp. 291 and 293), and (c) from 1987b (p. 200). Copyright ©1987 Scott, Foresman & Co. Reproduced by permission.

correct answers. Numerical relationships such as "8 + 1 + 5 = 14" have nothing to do with space.

Presenting One Technique at a Time

We have just seen that, in traditional math programs, two-digit addition with no "renaming" is introduced in first grade, while two-digit addition with one "renaming" is introduced in second grade. I will argue shortly that all kinds of one- and two-digit addition problems such as the following ought to be introduced at about the same time, in second grade, so that children can figure out how tens and ones and place value "work":

$$
\begin{array}{cccc}
9 & 12 & 13 & 13 \\
+5 & +\ 8 & +13 & +18 \\
\end{array}
$$

THE NCTM'S APPROACH

As pointed out in Chapter 4, the National Council of Teachers of Mathematics (NCTM, 1988) defines goals and objectives very differently from the scope-and-sequence approach of traditional textbook writers. The main differences are that the NCTM has a much broader vision of school mathematics and that they focus on the learner rather than exclusively on mathematics.

The NCTM document divides the K–12 range into three age groups (grades K–4, 5–8, and 9–12) and begins by providing 13 or 14 standards for each of the three groups. The first eight of the K–4 standards are listed here because of their relevance to second-grade arithmetic (NCTM, July, 1988, Table of Contents):

Standard 1. Mathematics As Problem Solving
Standard 2. Mathematics As Communication
Standard 3. Mathematics As Reasoning
Standard 4. Mathematical Connections
Standard 5. Estimation
Standard 6. Number Sense and Numeration
Standard 7. Concepts of Whole Number Operations
Standard 8. Whole Number Computation

These standards are a far cry from the traditional scope-and-sequence perspective. In traditional texts, computation comes first and problem solving, last. The NCTM Standards are conceived in reverse order.

The Standards' five general goals for students are the following, as stated in the previous chapter: "(1) that they learn to value mathematics, (2) that they become confident in their ability to do mathematics, (3) that they become mathematical problem solvers, (4) that they learn to communicate mathematically, and (5) that they learn to reason mathematically" (July, 1988, p. 4). These goals, particularly those pertaining to students' confidence and ability to reason, are very different from those found in all the textbook series today.

Prominent in the NCTM document are discussions of "number sense," "operation sense," and "informal, intuitive notions," the development of which does not appear anywhere in traditional textbooks. The NCTM document also makes the following statement that departs radically from the emphasis of traditional textbooks: "Clearly, paper-and-pencil computation cannot continue to dominate the curriculum . . ." (July, 1988, p. 45).

Unlike the approach of traditional textbooks, the NCTM Standards are based on a large body of research on children's learning of mathematics. The changes recommended are a giant step in the right direction. While I am in general agreement with these recommendations, I believe that they do not go far enough. My criticism of the K–4 Standards is that they are too vague and are still rooted in empiricism. Below is an explanation of this remark.

The most specific statement in the NCTM document pertaining to the ages at which mastery of "basic facts" can be expected is the following: "Children should master the basic facts of arithmetic that are essential components of fluency with paper-and-pencil and mental computation, and with estimation. At the same time, however, mastery should not be expected too soon" (July, 1988, p. 48). This is a vague and meaningless statement compared to the following excerpt from an article by two members of the group who worked on the K–4 Standards (Thompson & Rathmell, 1988). Similar recommendations made in the 1987 draft of the Standards did not appear in the final document.

> Many classroom teachers have been frustrated in trying to teach mathematical concepts and skills before their students are developmentally ready. This instruction often consumes large amounts of time, and children resort to rote memorization of definitions and rules in order to be successful. . . . Accordingly, the Standards have shifted several topics to more appropriate grade levels. For example, the introduction of place value is now recommended for second grade, and a focus on numbers greater than four digits is not recommended until after fourth grade. Furthermore, mastery of the basic addition and subtraction facts has been delayed until third grade, and mastery of the basic multiplication and division facts has been delayed until fourth grade. [p. 18]

I would have applauded these recommendations if they had been retained in the final version of the Standards.

Empiricism, it will be recalled, is the belief that knowledge has its source in external reality and that the child acquires it by internalizing it through the senses. Piaget proved with numerous experiments, such as the one with chips described at the beginning of Chapter 1 (Inhelder & Piaget, 1963), that logico-mathematical knowledge has its source inside the child, who constructs relationships and imposes them on objects. The essential activity in the child's creation of logico-mathematical knowledge is constructive abstraction, which is completely absent from the NCTM document.

There are two areas in which the Standards particularly reveal the empiricist assumptions of its authors. One is the frequent allusion to "basic facts," and the other concerns paper-and-pencil algorithms.

"Basic Facts"

As stated in Chapter 1, there is no such thing as a "number fact," from the standpoint of Piaget's theory. A fact is observable, but a number is not. For example, six cookies are observable, but the concept of "six" is not. Number concepts are relationships constructed by each child through constructive abstraction. It follows that $6 + 2 = 8$ is not a fact but a relationship constructed by each child, on the relationships he or she has constructed before.

Piaget (Piaget & Inhelder, 1948/1967) stated that even the facts that a child can "read" from reality depend on his level of logico-mathematical knowledge. The memory task cited in Chapter 1 involving the observation that the same six chips cover $3 + 3$, $1 + 2 + 3$, and $1 + 5$ illustrates this point. The children who could establish the equivalence of "$1 + 2 + 3$," "$3 + 3$," and "$1 + 5$" could remember the observed facts correctly. Those who could not, on the other hand, could not remember the same observed facts.

It is essential for educators to understand the nature of logico-mathematical knowledge, because teachers who believe that logico-mathematical knowledge consists of facts will present "facts" or facilitate children's observation of "facts," rather than focusing on their thinking.

Paper-and-Pencil Algorithms

Below is an excerpt from the NCTM Standards concerning the "connections" to be made for mastery of paper-and-pencil algorithms.

Placing computation in a problem-solving context motivates students to learn computational skills and provides an impetus for mastery of paper-and-pencil algorithms. Initial use of physical materials, such as base 10 blocks or bundling sticks, can be carefully connected to concrete models and then finally, to symbolic work. The following example (Figure 5.3) illustrates the connections that can be made between concrete materials and a paper-and-pencil algorithm. (July, 1988, p. 46)

The example shown in Figure 5.3 is an empiricist approach that attempts to explain the algorithm to children from the outside. The only children who will understand this explanation are those who have already constructed the system of tens on the system of ones, through constructive abstraction. As for the term "connection" in the preceding quote, it is not clear who is making these connections, or associations. My interpretation is that they are made by the teacher, with the hope that children will internalize them. I will argue shortly that Piaget's constructivism suggests the desirability of encouraging children to invent their own procedures rather than teaching algorithms and explaining them with base-10 blocks.

Unlike traditional textbooks, the NCTM Standards recommend the teaching of estimation and mental arithmetic. While this recommendation is progressive, it, too, suffers from the empiricist assumption according to which every procedure has to be taught from the outside. The following quote concerning "front-end estimation" is an example of an empiricist approach:

Children also should be taught specific strategies to aid them in making *computational* estimation. A child who needs to evaluate 243 + 479 might estimate by thinking: "200 and 400 is 600, 43 and 79 is over a

Figure 5.3.   An attempt to explain "regrouping."

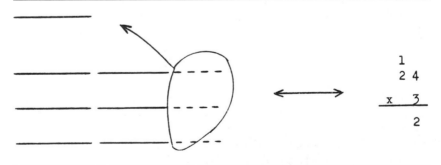

hundred, so the sum is a little more than 700." This is "front-end estimation." (July, 1988, p. 36)

The teaching of "front-end estimation" is superfluous when children are
allowed to invent their own procedures. If they are not made to add the
ones first, they universally add the hundreds first, before proceeding to
the tens and then to the ones.

ALTERNATIVE APPROACH, BASED ON PIAGET'S THEORY

With the preceding discussion as background, I explain in this section
how I approach place value and addition, subtraction, multiplication, and
division with two-digit numbers. My stance in defining objectives is similar to that of the NCTM in that I, too, base my conceptualization on
research about children's learning of arithmetic. The difference is that I
have studied Piaget's research and theory sufficiently to be convinced of
the validity of constructivism.

As discussed in Chapter 1, constructivism is the theory stating that
children build their knowledge, especially logico-mathematical knowledge, by construction from the inside, rather than by internalization from
the environment. An essential part of Piagetian constructivism is the
three kinds of knowledge he distinguishes on the basis of their ultimate
sources. His distinction between physical knowledge and logico-
mathematical knowledge convinced me that the source of the latter is not
observable facts or materials such as base-10 blocks. The difference he
pointed out between social knowledge and logico-mathematical knowledge convinced me that the teacher's explanation or the feedback he or
she provides is not the source of logico-mathematical knowledge, either.
In the logico-mathematical realm, the source of feedback for children is
the coherence of the relationships they themselves make, which gives
them the feeling that something *makes sense*. The distinction between
social and logico-mathematical knowledge also helped me understand
that, while the symbols involved in doing arithmetic—for example, in
$8 + 5 = (8 + 2) + 3$—are teachable through social transmission, the
underlying reasoning is not.

The objectives that will be discussed shortly are based also on 4 years
of experience (1984–1988) at Hall-Kent School with three teachers of second grade (as well as a dozen other teachers of grades K, 1, and 3). The
three teachers each had a different group of second graders every year.
By September 1986, the children who arrived in second grade had not
had any traditional instruction in kindergarten and first grade. Their math

education had consisted of the two kinds of activities described in *Number in Preschool and Kindergarten* (Kamii, 1982), *Group Games in Early Education* (Kamii & DeVries, 1980), and *Young Children Reinvent Arithmetic* (Kamii, 1985), namely, the use of situations in daily living and group games.

I did not have specific objectives for second graders when I began to work at Hall-Kent School. When some children solved a problem on their own, we gave them a harder problem, to find out what they might invent. For example, if at least some children could do 13 + 13, we asked them how they might do 12 + 8 and, later, 13 + 17. If at least some could do 4 × 6 in a "story" problem, we likewise asked them how they might do 8 × 6 and 4 × 16 in other story problems.

Some of the results of this kind of teaching can be seen in Chapter 10 on evaluation. The general conclusions that my colleagues and I have reached, in a nutshell, are (1) that the range of individual differences increases when children are encouraged to invent their own procedures and (2) that some topics are harder while others are easier than they are assumed to be by traditional math educators. For example, in traditional instruction, mastery of subtraction by using "regrouping" is expected in second grade, but this expectation appears to be more appropriate for third or fourth graders. On the other hand, nearly half of our second graders have invented negative numbers, which do not appear at all in elementary textbooks. While inventing ways of solving problems such as

$$\frac{\begin{array}{r}36\\-18\end{array}}{}$$

our second graders said, "Take 10 from 30, and that's 20. Take 8 from 6, and that's 2 in the hole (or 2 below 0). So I take 2 from the 20, and the answer is 18." At this point, all the teacher had to do was to supply a bit of social knowledge, the term *negative 2*.

My objectives for second grade are grouped into the following five categories:

1. Addition of one-digit numbers
2. Place value and addition of two-digit numbers
3. Subtraction of one- and two-digit numbers
4. Multiplication
5. Division

These were arrived at through experience. When the great majority of our second graders could invent a procedure, we concluded that it was an appropriate objective for them. For example, addition of two-digit numbers was invented by the great majority of our second graders every year. For children who are at lower or higher developmental levels than the Hall-Kent children, these objectives may not be appropriate.

Addition of One-Digit Numbers

The objective for single-digit addition stated in *Young Children Reinvent Arithmetic* (Kamii, 1985) is that "children engage in the mental action of operating on numbers and remember the results of these actions" (p. 65). I now think that part of this statement is too limited and that this objective should be changed to the following:

> *that children act on numbers additively and construct a network of numerical relationships.*

Part of this network has been illustrated by Labinowicz (1985) and is reproduced in Figure 5.4. Creation of this network is very different from the objective of "remembering the results" of various actions. My previous conceptualization was still too much like the traditional objective of remembering isolated "facts."

"Seven" is at first just a number concept the child has in relation to the ideas of "one," "two," "three," "four," and so forth. As the child operates on these numbers, he or she comes to know "seven" in all the different ways presented in Figure 5.4. The child who has constructed this kind of network in his or her mind can use it to change $7 + 5$, for example, to $(7 + 3) + 2$ or to $(5 + 5) + 2$. The child can also change $7 + 8$ to $(7 + 7) + 1$ or to $(8 + 2) + 5$. A network of numerical relationships will serve the child throughout life in all the other mathematical operations as well.

Place Value and Addition of Two-Digit Numbers

Traditional textbooks recommend the teaching of place value in first grade, before the introduction of double-column addition that does not require "regrouping." This teaching of place value is repeated in second grade, prior to the reintroduction of double-column addition and the teaching of "regrouping."

As stated in Chapter 2, research into children's thinking about tens and ones led me to hypothesize that it might be possible for children in second grade to understand place value. However, it seemed best to introduce place value by encouraging children to use it in a meaningful context. After all, all children already know in first grade that the numeral for nine is 9, that the numeral for ten is 10, and that the series continues with 11, 12, 13, and so on. Children learn to walk by walking, and to talk

Figure 5.4. An example of the network of numerical relationships.

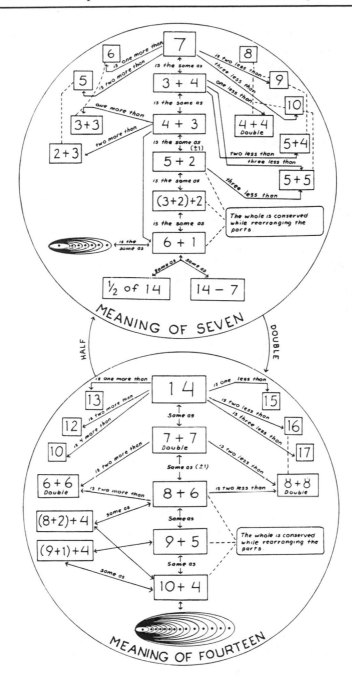

From *Learning From Children: New Beginnings for Teaching Numerical Thinking* by E. Labinow-icz, 1985, p. 99. Reproduced by permission of Addison-Wesley Publishing Company.

by talking, without lessons on prerequisite skills or grammar. It seemed best, therefore, to encourage them to figure out how place value "worked" while inventing their own ways of solving problems such as 9 + 5, 10 + 10, and 10 + 12. My hypothesis was confirmed every year.

My objective for the addition of two-digit numbers therefore is as follows:

> *that children invent their own procedures for two-digit addition and learn place value in the process.*

The rationale for this objective has been discussed at length in Chapters 1 and 2. Young children understand the procedures *they* invent, but not the algorithms they memorize in traditional instruction (see Chapter 10). Children are also more likely to *remember* the procedures *they* invent, thereby making repeated reviews unnecessary. Furthermore, the procedures they invent are rooted deeply in their intuition and develop their "number sense" and ability to make reasonable estimates.

Unlike traditional instruction, in my approach children are presented with problems that require "regrouping" at about the same time as addition that does not require it. When second graders are not told how to add two-digit numbers, the procedures they usually invent for problems such as

$$\begin{array}{r} 13 \\ + 13 \\ \hline \end{array}$$

are the following:

10 + 10 = 20	10 + 10 = 20
3 + 3 = 6	20 + 3 = 23
20 + 6 = 26	23 + 3 = 26

The procedures they generally invent for problems requiring "regrouping," such as

$$\begin{array}{r} 18 \\ + 13 \\ \hline \end{array}$$

include

10 + 10 = 20	10 + 10 = 20	10 + 10 = 20
8 + 3 = 11	20 + 8 = 28	8 + 2 = another ten
20 + 10 = 30	28 + 3 = 31	20 + 10 = 30
30 + 1 = 31		30 + 1 = 31

Note that children naturally think about tens and figure out how place value "works," without a single lesson with bundles of straws, base-10 blocks, or place-value boxes.

Many second graders can add three- and four-digit numbers. We, of course, challenge these children when they want to be challenged. The extent to which they handle multi-digit addition problems such as

$$\begin{array}{r} 1,568 \\ +\,2,896 \\ \hline \end{array}$$

can be seen in Chapter 6. Since they add multi-digit numbers in their heads, without paper and pencil, many second graders are better at mental arithmetic than most of the adults I know, including myself.

Subtraction of One- and Two-Digit Numbers

In traditional textbooks, subtraction comes immediately after addition, as the mere inverse of addition. As stated in *Young Children Reinvent Arithmetic* (Kamii, 1985), however, subtraction is much harder for young children than is usually assumed. In fact, the general sequence of learning perhaps ought to be addition, multiplication, subtraction, and division.

Let us begin with some facts from research. At Hall-Kent School in May 1987 only 34% of the third graders (all of whom had reinvented arithmetic without traditional instruction) got the answer of 27 for the following problem:

$$\begin{array}{r} 43 \\ -\,16 \\ \hline \end{array}$$

The procedures they used were usually among the following:

$40 - 10 = 30$	$40 - 10 = 30$	$40 - 10 = 30$
$30 - 6 = 24$	$30 + 3 = 33$	$3 - 6 = 3$ in the hole
$24 + 3 = 27$	$33 - 6 = 27$	$30 - 3 = 27$

About 40% of the same group got the familiar, incorrect answer of 33 by subtracting the smaller number in each column from the larger one. When the interviewer expressed dissatisfaction, however, most of these children reconsidered their procedure and corrected themselves. These facts suggest that the difficulty of subtraction requiring "borrowing" lies in part-whole relationships, and that mastery of this task may be an appropriate objective for third or fourth grade.

Reporting on the Second National Assessment of Educational Progress

(NAEP), Carpenter, Corbitt, Kepner, Lindquist, and Reys (1980) stated that only about 65% of the 9-year-olds in third and fourth grade could solve "a simple subtraction exercise requiring regrouping; by age 13 over 90 percent of the students could solve the problem" (p. 11). The following interpretation they give of these and other findings is highly significant:

> The results in the addition and subtraction exercises may have several implications for the instruction of young children. First, performance does improve with age, even without a heavy emphasis on addition and subtraction computation in the upper grades. It is important to realize that this change is occurring and that unreasonable mastery levels should not be set for younger children. [p. 11]

The longitudinal perspective in this excerpt is unusual and refreshing. Children do construct mathematics over many years.

The percentages improved by the Fourth National Assessment, with 70% of third graders and 94% of seventh graders getting the correct answer to a similar problem (Kouba et al., 1988). These numbers cannot be used for the definition of objectives because they probably reflect the heavy use of drill resulting from the pressure for higher test scores that has spread all over the country in recent years.

Finally, an important part of our knowledge base is teachers' observation. Many outstanding teachers of fourth grade with many years of experience have told me that "borrowing" in subtraction is still hard for many fourth graders. Based on his interview research and NAEP data, Labinowicz (1985) states that while two- and three-digit subtraction is now expected in second and third grade across the nation, "a reexamination of both teaching methods and grade placement is appropriate" (p. 357). I agree with him and formulate the following objective for two-digit subtraction in second grade:

> *that children who are able to will invent their own procedures for subtraction, with and without "regrouping."*

Single-digit subtraction is thus not a separate objective in my approach. Single-digit subtraction becomes easier as the child's addition and network of relationships (refer to Figure 5.3) become more solid. The way to "teach" one-digit subtraction seems to be to encourage children's construction of this network.

Multiplication

In November, Linda Joseph, in her second-grade class at Hall-Kent School, said, "Let's pretend that Adam, Brad, Cindy, and Dana (pointing to four people in the class) each have eight stickers. How many stickers would there be all together?" The children said, "That's 4 times 8" and got their answer by doubling 8 and doubling the double (8 + 8 = 16 and 16 + 16 = 32).

Linda kept giving harder and harder story problems such as the following: There are 21 children here today. How much money would I collect if everybody ordered a pencil with his or her name on it that costs 46 cents each? Most of the children got the answer by writing 46 21 times and laboriously adding the figures up. Some got the total for 10 forty-sixes, doubled the total, and added 46.

The objective for multiplication that I suggest for second grade is therefore the following:

> *that children invent their own procedures for solving story problems involving multiplicative thinking.*

Note that traditional second-grade books present double-column addition early in the school year and multiplication of small numbers toward the end of the year. By contrast, my colleagues and I present multiplication with small numbers early in second grade, along with all the other operations.

Small products such as 3 × 25¢ = 75¢, 4 × 3 = 12, and 4 × 5 = 20 become part of children's repertoires as they count money and play games repeatedly. Note that my objective is neither that they know the multiplication tables nor that they become able to write correct answers by using the "correct" procedure. Rather, it is that they think about the problem and figure out the answer in whatever way they can. They will eventually invent faster ways, and there is no reason to tell them that they can solve multiplication problems only by using multiplication.

Division

A mother gave Linda a check for $5.75 for her child's birthday celebration and asked Linda to use it to get a popsicle for everybody in the class. Since everybody knew that the cafeteria sold popsicles for 25¢, Linda told the class, "I have to know *right now* if 5 dollars and 75 cents is enough to get a popsicle for everybody who is here today."

The children counted four members of the class and said, "That's one dollar." They counted four more members and said, "That's two dollars." They continued on to three, four, and five dollars, as they counted four more children each time. There were two children and the teacher left, and everybody agreed that there was exactly the right amount of money to get a popsicle for everybody.

The children did not divide $5.75 by 25¢ or by 23 people, but we were very impressed by their resourcefulness. Children often surprise us by inventing ways that we have not imagined. In this example, they used multiplication (4 × 25¢) and addition ($1 + $1 + $1, etc.) ingeniously. Note that second graders think positively and use addition and multiplication. They hardly ever think negatively and seldom use subtraction (see Kamii, 1985, Chapter 6, for further detail).

Division should grow out of these real-life situations and story problems. My objective for division in second grade is as follows:

> *that children invent their own procedures for solving story problems involving division.*

My objective, once again, reflects my conviction that children should be allowed to think in their own ways so that they will later invent more efficient techniques, out of their own logic.

CONCLUSION

The major difference between my objectives and those of traditional textbook series is that, while traditional instruction tries to teach one specific technique after another, I do not advocate teaching children how to do anything. Instead of teaching how to add, subtract, multiply, and divide, my colleagues and I encourage children to do their own thinking about math problems and to construct more efficient procedures for solving them out of their own ways of thinking. It may seem like a waste of time to let children add 46 21 times, but we save time in the long run because traditional instruction results in mindless obedience to rules (see Chapter 10), repeated review, and loss of confidence.

Another difference between my objectives and those of traditional instruction is that mine are stated in general rather than specific terms. The reason is that children's construction of logico-mathematical knowledge cannot be directly "caused" in specific ways. While surface behaviors can be modified specifically from the outside, the child's process of constructive abstraction can only be stimulated indirectly.

The NCTM Standards (July, 1988) are a giant step in the right direction. I applaud their reversal of the traditional sequence of beginning with computation and ending with problem solving. However, this document still advocates the teaching of algorithms as if logico-mathematical knowledge offered mere "connections" between "physical materials, such as base-10 blocks or bundling sticks" and paper-and-pencil procedures. Rather than trying to help children make "connections" between physical knowledge and social knowledge (mathematical symbols), I advocate children's construction of logico-mathematical knowledge. The source of logico-mathematical knowledge is inside the child, and our efforts must aim at constructive abstraction rather than at the child's observation, manipulation, and representation of observable facts.

Part III

ACTIVITIES

CHAPTER 6

Discussions of Computational and Story Problems

with Linda Joseph

Many teachers ask, "What do you *do* to get children to reinvent arithmetic, after throwing out the textbook and workbooks?" For kindergarten and first grade (Kamii, 1982, 1985) my answer to this question was that we use two kinds of activities—situations in daily living, such as voting; and games, such as board games with dice. We have added a third kind of activity in second grade: teacher-initiated discussions of computational and story problems. This chapter is devoted to these discussions. In Chapter 7, Linda Joseph describes the use of situations in daily living and other activities. Group games are then presented in Chapter 8.

Ways of adding two-digit numbers are very hard for second graders to invent, even when no regrouping is required. This is why the teacher takes the initiative to present the right kind of problem at the right time, depending on where in their development of logico-mathematical knowledge particular children are. Generally, about half of the math period is spend on these discussions and the other half on games.

The discussions begin by the teacher's putting a problem on the chalkboard, such as

$$\begin{array}{r} 18 \\ +13 \\ \hline \end{array}$$

and asking children, "What's a good way to solve this problem?" It is important for the teacher to follow this with wait time, to encourage all the children to think. When most of the hands are up, the teacher calls on individual children and writes all the different answers on the board, such as 21, 31, 211, and 13. (Children usually say "Agree!" or "Disagree!" as the teacher writes each answer.)

Being careful not to say that an answer is right or wrong, the teacher then asks for volunteers to explain how they got their answers. As the volunteer explains his or her reasoning, the teacher writes each step on the board and encourages the group to agree or disagree with it. For example, if a volunteer says, "Ten and 10 is 20," the teacher may point to each 1 (in 18 and 13) and write the child's ideas to the side as follows:

$$
\begin{array}{rr}
10 & 18 \\
+\ 10 & +\ 13 \\
\hline
20 &
\end{array}
$$

If the child then says, "I take 2 from the 3 and put it with the 8," the teacher writes -2 and $+2$, as follows:

$$
\begin{array}{rl}
10 & 18\ +2 \\
+\ 10 & +\ 13\ -2 \\
\hline
20 &
\end{array}
$$

If the child continues with "That's another 10," the teacher points to the 8 and $+2$ and writes 10, as shown below:

$$
\begin{array}{rl}
10 & 18\ +2 \\
+\ 10 & +\ 13\ -2 \\
\hline
20 & \\
10 &
\end{array}
$$

If the child's next statement is "Twenty and 10 is 30," the teacher erases all the 10s, the plus sign, the line, and the 2 of 20, changing the latter to 3, with the following result:

$$
\begin{array}{rl}
& 18\ +2 \\
& +\ 13\ -2 \\
30 & \hline
\end{array}
$$

If the child then says, "and 1 more is 31," the teacher points to "$3 - 2$," erases the 0 of 30, and changes it to 1, with the following result:

$$
\begin{array}{rl}
& 18\ +2 \\
& +\ 13\ -2 \\
31 & \hline
\end{array}
$$

The teacher then writes 31 under the double-column problem.

The teacher thus erases and writes on the board for two purposes: to let the student know what the teacher understands from the student's statements, and to help the rest of the class follow the explanation. The teacher refrains from saying that an answer is right or wrong and instead encourages the exchange of ideas among children.

The teacher then asks individual children to present all the different ways in which they got the answer. Two other procedures children often invent for the preceding problem are

$$10 + 10 = 20 \qquad 10 + 10 = 20$$
$$8 + 3 = 11 \qquad 20 + 8 = 28$$
$$20 + 10 = 30 \qquad 28 + 3 = 31$$
$$30 + 1 = 31$$

PRINCIPLES OF TEACHING

The principles of teaching followed by the teacher so far are the following:

1. Encourage children to invent their own procedures rather than showing them how to solve problems.
2. Encourage children to invent many different ways of solving the same problem.
3. Refrain from reinforcing correct answers and correcting wrong ones, and instead encourage the exchange of points of view among children.
4. Encourage children to think rather than to write, and write on the chalkboard for them to facilitate the exchange of viewpoints.

The reason for the first two principles is, again, that logico-mathematical knowledge must be constructed by each child. Operations consist of reasoning, and children can use their own natural ability to figure out how to solve computational problems. They also build a better foundation for further learning by inventing their own procedures.

The third principle of teaching is derived from the importance of social interaction to the child's construction of logico-mathematical knowledge. As explained in Chapters 3 and 4, the construction of logico-mathematical knowledge is stimulated by exchanges of points of view. The history of science attests to the importance of debate in adults' creation of knowledge. Children, too, must be encouraged to determine truth for themselves through debate, rather than through reward and punishment.

The fourth principle of teaching flows from the third one and the objective of focusing on children's thinking rather than their writing. As explained in Chapters 1 and 5, mathematical symbols belong to social (conventional) knowledge, and our focus should be on logico-mathematical knowledge, or thinking. By requiring children to write symbols in specific spots, traditional instruction makes them dependent on paper and pencil as well as on ready-made rules.

Our approach has been heavily influenced by Madell (1985), who said that, when children are encouraged to do double-column addition in their own natural way, "they *universally* proceed from left to right" (p. 21). With respect to the problem

$$36$$
$$+46$$

for example, he states the following:

> Invariably, in a problem like this, the seven- and eight-year-olds first compute the tens. The details vary:
> a) Some will actually record a 7 in the tens column before looking at the ones. These children then come back and erase.
> b) Others, having arrived at 7 as the sum of 3 and 4, do not record that 7 before checking the ones column to see if it contains another ten.
> c) A few of the most sophisticated students check the ones first. Noting (often by estimation) that there are more than 10 ones in the ones column, they come back to sum the tens and record 8 before returning to the ones and the last detail of the computation.
> This last process is the closest that the children get on their own to the standard right-to-left procedure. Even for the addition of 3- and 4-digit numbers where a right-to-left process would seem more efficient, the children uniformly prefer the other direction. [p. 21]

Madell (1985) used base-10 blocks but, instead, we encourage children to *think* about tens and ones, because we believe that the source of logico-mathematical knowledge is in thinking, not in objects. Anther difference between Madell's approach and ours is that we do not think or talk about "the sum of 3 and 4" when adding 36 and 46. Instead, we think and talk about "the sum of 30 and 40." If a child in our classrooms talks about the sum of 3 and 4 in such a situation, some others may immediately exclaim, "Disagree!" If no one disagrees, the teacher will challenge the children by saying, "I get 19 for 3 plus 4 plus 6 plus 6. How did you get 82?" We thus do not teach place value directly, but instead give many opportunities for children to use what they know to figure out how place value works. For example, all second graders know that $10 + 10 = 20$ (Kamii, 1985, p. 76), and we encourage them to use this knowledge to figure out what $10 + 12$ might be.

In the discussions, more advanced children literally invent their own ways of doing double-column addition. Others listen to these inventions and adopt them if and when they want to. It can, therefore, be said that not all children reinvent double-column addition. I argue, however, that they all reinvent it because they are free not to accept any idea unless *they* decide that an idea makes sense to them. In our classes some children listen to discussions with lost looks for 4 or even 7 months, but, when they finally begin to participate, we can tell that they have invented the reasoning of double-column addition for themselves.

The questions often asked by visitors are, How do you get these discussions started? How do you sequence the problems? and Why do you work with the whole class when everybody else is saying that teachers should work with small groups? These questions will be answered in the rest of the chapter, as we take a look at some of the activities Linda Joseph has been using in her classroom.

GETTING STARTED[1]

I begin the year with a lively game that the entire class plays, called Around the World. In it, two children at a time compete to see who can give the sum of two numbers faster, after I show a flashcard. The first two children stand up to compete. The winner then stands behind (or next to) the third child, and these two wait for me to show the next flashcard. The one who wins then stands behind the fourth child, and so on, until everybody has had a chance to compete. A child who defeats all others and makes it back to his or her seat by moving from classmate to classmate is the champion who has gone "around the world."

We play this game for about 30 minutes. I then go to the board and say, "I noticed that Tom[2] answered this question quickly," and write a problem such as the following on the board:

$$
\begin{array}{r}
9 \\
+5 \\
\hline
\end{array}
$$

---

[1] The remainder of this chapter is authored by Linda Joseph, recounted directly from her experiences as a second-grade teacher at Hall-Kent Elementary School.

[2] The real names of all the children mentioned in this book have been changed to protect their privacy.

"Can anyone think of a fast way to get the answer?" One child may say, "You can count it fast in your head," and another may say, "Take 1 off the 5 and put it with the 9." Following the child's statement, I write -1 and $+1$ as shown, so that everybody can decide if this procedure makes sense:

$$\begin{array}{r} 9 \; +1 \\ +5 \; -1 \\ \hline \end{array}$$

"That's 10," the child continues, and I add to the computation as follows:

$$\begin{array}{r} 9 \; +1 \; = 10 \\ +5 \; -1 \\ \hline \end{array}$$

As the child says, "And 4 more is 14," I add these calculations, as shown:

$$\begin{array}{r} 9 \; +1 \; = 10 \\ +5 \; -1 \; = \; 4 \\ \hline 14 \end{array}$$

I may sometimes write much less and follow the same child by writing only the following:

$$\begin{array}{rr} \cancel{9} & 10 \\ +\cancel{5} & 4 \\ \hline 14 & \end{array}$$

When all alternative procedures have been offered, I go on to another problem, for example,

$$\begin{array}{r} 8 \\ +7 \\ \hline \end{array}$$

To a problem such as this, some children respond, "I know 8 and 8 is 16; so take 1 off and it's 15." Others will then agree that doubles are easy, and I encourage them to use what they already know to go on from there. Other ways that children often invent are

$$(7 + 7) + 1$$
$$(8 + 2) + 5$$
$$(7 + 3) + 5$$

The reason for all this discussion of different ways of computing is to emphasize the process of thinking rather than merely getting right answers. I also want children to listen to each other and to adopt the ideas that appeal to them.

After a few days of beginning the math hour by playing Around the World, I stop using this game and go directly to a few problems, such as

$$\begin{array}{r} 2 \\ +3 \\ \hline \end{array} \qquad \begin{array}{r} 5 \\ +3 \\ \hline \end{array} \qquad \begin{array}{r} 3 \\ +6 \\ \hline \end{array}$$

I begin the hour with easy problems whose sums are less than 10, so that all children have a chance to feel successful. The general sequence I keep in mind is the following:

1. Single-digit problems up to 9 + 9. I pay particular attention to numbers that are likely to suggest the use of doubles, such as 5 + 6, and of 10, such as 8 + 3.
2. "Ragged-column" problems with "10-plus" addends that do not need "regrouping," up to a sum of 19. By "10-plus" addends, I mean numbers from 11 to 19. Almost all children construct *the system of ones* up to 19 by the end of second grade (Kamii, 1986). For many of them, 14, for instance, is 14 *ones*, and not 1 ten and 4 ones (also see Madell, 1985). Examples include

$$\begin{array}{r} 10 \\ +5 \\ \hline \end{array} \qquad \begin{array}{r} 12 \\ +6 \\ \hline \end{array}$$

3. "Ragged-column" and double-column problems with and without "re-grouping." Examples include

$$\begin{array}{r} 16 \\ +4 \\ \hline \end{array} \qquad \begin{array}{r} 10 \\ +12 \\ \hline \end{array} \qquad \begin{array}{r} 13 \\ +13 \\ \hline \end{array} \qquad \begin{array}{r} 19 \\ +12 \\ \hline \end{array}$$

During each math hour, I mix problems that require "regrouping" and those that do not. One of the reasons is that children might otherwise construct the rule (or trick) of merely adding each column as ones. I pay particular attention to combinations that make 10 by using 10-plus addends, such as 17 + 3 and 12 + 8. I then go on to larger addends, such as 43 + 7, 38 + 5, and 38 + 13.
4. Problems involving many numbers. Examples include

$$\begin{array}{r} 7 \\ 4 \\ 8 \\ 3 \\ +2 \\ \hline \end{array}$$

Again, I pay particular attention to combinations that make 10, such as 7 + 3 and 8 + 2 in the preceding example.

I go as far as the children are able during each hour. The practice of going through a variety of problems during each math hour is in contrast to textbook instruction, which focuses on only one type of exercise each day (such as double-column addition without regrouping). I prefer to offer variety partly because children benefit from hearing discussions of problems they think are too hard for them, as well as of those they can solve. Almost every day, someone will attempt a new and harder type of problem for the first time, and I am ecstatic when this happens.

I sometimes invite small groups to work on problems with me, while others play games; however, I insist on having the entire class for the discussions, because the less advanced children benefit from listening to the arguments of the more advanced children.

For example, one day in mid-September an advanced child begged for "something harder, something in the hundreds." So I wrote the following problem for him:

$$\begin{array}{r} 73 \\ +38 \\ \hline \end{array}$$

Amazingly, he gave the correct answer after a brief moment. When I asked how he got his answer, he said he had added 30 to 70 and gotten 100, and 11 more made 111.

I then decided to check the rest of the class for their method of tackling a type of problem they had probably never encountered before. So I wrote this problem on the board:

$$\begin{array}{r} 46 \\ +46 \\ \hline \end{array}$$

I walked around the room and had the children whisper their answers in my ear, and without comment, I listed them all on the board: 91, 92, 20, 81, and 812.

After sufficient wait time, I said to the class, "Now I want you to tell me how you reached your answers." Pointing to the number 812, I asked "Who got this answer?" When a student identified herself, I asked her where she had begun. She said, "Four plus 4 is 8 and 6 plus 6 is 12; so the answer is 812." I asked the class if they agreed, and many exclaimed that they did not. "Why not?" I inquired, and Jay said, "That's not 4, that's 40!"

Concerned that I was getting to the correct answer too quickly, I pointed to the number 20 and asked, "Who got this answer?" Two children raised their hands and offered two different explanations. One said, "Four and 4 is 8, and 6 and 6 is 12, so 8 and 12 is 20." The other explained, "Four and 6 is 10, and 4 and 6 makes another 10, so 10 and 10 is 20." I responded that Jay had just said that the 4 didn't mean 4, but 40, and repeated the original problem: "How much is 46 and 46?" Several hands went up, and some said, "Oh! It has to be 80!" One went on to say, "Take 10 from 12 and add it to 80, and you get 90, and 2 left over is 92." At this point several children asked that their original answers be erased.

THREE EXAMPLES OF MATH SESSIONS

Having discussed principles of teaching and children's inventions in general, I would now like to sketch how I proceed each day and how the discussions change during the course of a year. To do this, I present three examples of sessions that took place in October, February, and May one year.

October 1

This was one of the days of filming to make the videotape, *Double-Column Addition: A Teacher Uses Piaget's Theory* (Kamii & Knight, 1987). The problems I put on the board on this day, one at a time, were the following:

$$
\begin{array}{ccc}
9 & 8 & 6 \\
+6 & +7 & 4 \\
& & +2 \\
\\
3 & 5 & 13 \\
6 & 4 & +13 \\
+1 & 3 & \\
& +2 & \\
\\
17 & 26 & 4 \\
+13 & +5 & \times 5 \\
\end{array}
$$

We spent about 25 minutes discussing all the different ways the children invented.

February 5

This was another day of filming for the videotape. I put the following problems on the board, one at a time, and spent about 30 minutes discussing all the different ways the children wanted to show off.

$$
\begin{array}{r} 4 \\ +4 \\ \hline \end{array}
\qquad
\begin{array}{r} 20 \\ +50 \\ \hline \end{array}
\qquad
\begin{array}{r} 24 \\ +53 \\ \hline \end{array}
$$

$$
\begin{array}{r} 29 \\ +35 \\ \hline \end{array}
\qquad
\begin{array}{r} 87 \\ +24 \\ \hline \end{array}
\qquad
\begin{array}{r} 420 \\ +346 \\ \hline \end{array}
$$

$$
\begin{array}{r} 2680 \\ +3319 \\ \hline \end{array}
\qquad
\begin{array}{r} 18 \\ -\ 7 \\ \hline \end{array}
\qquad
\begin{array}{r} 17 \\ -\ 9 \\ \hline \end{array}
$$

$$
\begin{array}{r} 26 \\ -17 \\ \hline \end{array}
\qquad
\begin{array}{r} 24 \\ -14 \\ \hline \end{array}
$$

I threw in the following story problem after the second subtraction problem: There are 65 second graders at Hall-Kent School, when we put all three second-grade classes together. Twenty-six of the second graders ordered chicken for lunch, and the rest ordered soup. How many are getting soup? The answers the children gave were 39 (eight children), 41 (five children), 34 (one child), and "Don't know" (nine children). When some children have no idea how to approach a problem, we discuss all the different ideas about how to set it up. So I ended up writing the following on the board:

$$
\begin{array}{r} 65 \\ -26 \\ \hline \end{array}
$$

Joyce announced that she got as far as $60 - 20 = 40$ but got stuck. Those who got 39 as the answer explained it in one of the following ways:

$$60 - 20 = 40 \qquad\qquad 60 - 20 = 40$$
$$40 - 6 = 34 \qquad\qquad 5 - 6 = 1 \text{ in the hole}$$
$$34 + 5 = 39 \qquad\qquad\qquad\quad \text{negative 1 or}$$
$$\qquad\qquad\qquad\qquad\qquad\quad 1 \text{ below } 0$$
$$\qquad\qquad\quad 40 - 1 = 39$$

The answer of 41 to such a problem is well known to all second- and third-grade teachers. Some of our children get this answer by dealing with the tens first, as follows: $60 - 20 = 40$, $6 - 5 = 1$, and $40 + 1 = 41$.

May 21

Most of the hour was spent on story problems, but I gave the following three computational problems first:

$$\begin{array}{ccc} 28 & 1{,}568 & 87 \\ +92 & +2{,}896 & -29 \end{array}$$

The first problem was easy for almost everybody, and about half of the children agreed that the way to solve the second problem was the following:

$$1{,}000 + 2{,}000 = 3{,}000$$
$$500 + 800 = 1{,}300$$
$$3{,}000 + 1{,}000 = 4{,}000$$
$$4{,}000 + 300 = 4{,}300$$
$$60 + 90 = 150$$
$$4{,}300 + 100 = 4{,}400$$
$$4{,}400 + 50 = 4{,}450$$
$$8 + 6 = 14$$
$$4{,}450 + 10 = 4{,}460$$
$$4{,}460 + 4 = 4{,}464$$

The subtraction problem $87 - 29$, demonstrated the usual difficulties. One-third of the class was fully confident, but the rest gave the usual kinds of answers: 91, 68, and 62.

"Let's go on to something else," I said, and went on to the following story problem: There are 3 flies. If each fly has 46 suction cups on each one of its feet, how many suction cups are there all together?

I immediately heard busy comments about whether the problem was 46×3 or 46×18. So I said, "Some people say the problem is 46 times 3, and some people say it is 46 times 18. Which one is it?" Someone answered, "Forty-six times 18 is right because each fly has 6 legs, and 6 and 6 and 6 is 18." There were lots of comments, and someone suggested, "Let's just go our own ways."

I went around the room to find out how the children were thinking, by looking at what they were writing. I then put the following answers vertically on the board, as the children announced them: 134, 138, 1,068, 876, 728, 148, and 828. Some children exclaimed "Disagree!" when they heard the smaller numbers. As a result, the children who got the first two answers felt the need to check them and later asked me to cross them out.

"Who can prove that their answer is right?" I asked. I chose three children to come to the board, one at a time. They had all used addition in a variety of ways.

Chuck said, "Forty, 40, 40, 40, and 40—that's 200," and I wrote,

$$
\begin{array}{r}
40 \\
40 \\
40 \\
40 \\
\underline{40} \\
200
\end{array}
$$

He went on to say, "Another five is 200, plus 200, and that's 400. We got rid of 10 of the 18. Five more is 600, and three more is 600 plus 120, and that's 720." Following his statements, I went on writing, as follows:

$$
\begin{array}{r}
40 \\
40 \\
40 \\
40 \\
\underline{40} \\
200 \\
\underline{200} \\
400 \\
\underline{200} \\
600 \\
\underline{120} \\
720
\end{array}
$$

Chuck then said, "Six, four times, is 12 and 12 and that's 24. Another 4 sixes is 48. That takes care of 8 of the 18 sixes. We need 10 more, and that's 48 and 12, which is 60. And put 60 with 48, and that's 108." Looking at the 720 I had written on the board, he then added 108 to it and announced that the answer was 828.

The second way of solving the problem was invented by Ellen and Cathy, who usually worked together. They started out by asking me to write "18 forty-sixes." (I encourage children to ask me to write on the board because they write so slowly that they lose the class's attention.) A summary of their procedure can be seen in Figure 6.1. Unlike Chuck, they used a greal deal of writing. When they were finished and saw that their answer was the same as Chuck's, they jumped up and down with joy.

The third way of solving the same problem was invented by George. He began by asking me to write 40 six times in a column, six more times,

Figure 6.1.   Ellen and Cathy's way of doing 46 × 18.

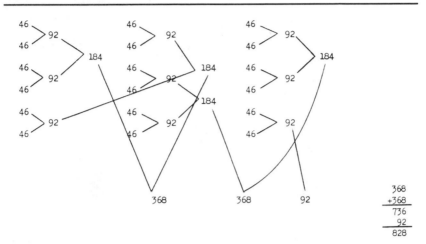

and six more times, always in a column. A summary of his procedure can be seen in Figure 6.2.

I went on to an easier problem: Let's suppose we have a beehive. In this beehive, there are 10 bees going to collect nectar. Each bee visits 36 flowers. How many trips did all the bees make, all together?

Somebody immediately yelled, "That's 10 times 36!" Four different ways of solving this problem were volunteered. Carol got 30 × 10 = 300 by counting by tens. She then added the sixes as shown in Figure 6.3 and announced the answer of 360.

Jerry's way was similar, but he used a lot of writing and started out by asking me to write 10 thirty-sixes. Figure 6.4 illustrates his procedure.

I asked, "Does anyone have a way that is the fastest?" George offered the following argument:

$$10 \times 10 = 100; \text{ so } 30 \times 10 = 300$$
$$6 \times 10 = 60$$
$$300 + 60 = 360$$

Cathy challenged him by saying, "Anything times 10 is the number with a zero. Always, all you have to do is add a zero to it. So 10 times 36 equals 360. That's all there's to it!" Surprised by this bit of knowledge Cathy had, I said, "I want you to prove to me that 10 times 36 is 360."

Cathy came to the board with Ellen, and the two wrote the number 10 thirty-six times all over the board. They first counted the top row, "Ten, 20, 30, 40, 50, 60, 70," and wrote 70 for it. They then repeated this pro-

Figure 6.2.   George's way of doing 46 × 18.

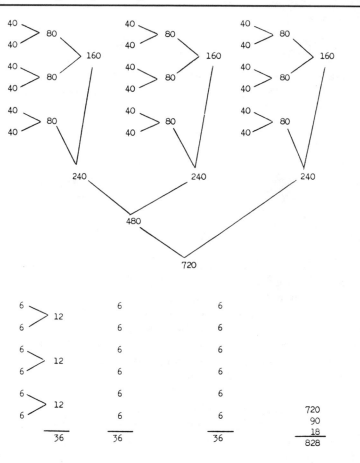

cedure twice but got confused and decided to start all over, from 10 to 360.

CONCLUSION

I would like to end this chapter with a few comments about what children write or do not write during these discussions. When they are not required to write anything, they are free to think. This is why I ask them to put everything away at the beginning of our discussions. As we get to

Figure 6.3. Part of Carol's work in computing 10 × 36.

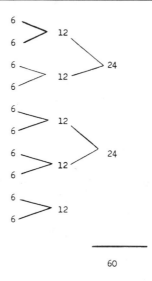

Figure 6.4. Jerry's way of doing 10 × 36.

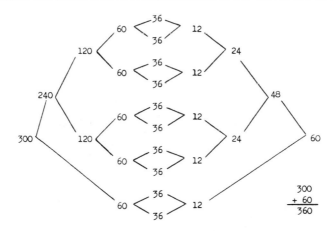

large addends in the hundreds or repeated addition such as 10 × 36, however, I see children writing on paper or on their desks. When they need to use writing to remember the results of their thinking, I let them use paper and pencil. This kind of writing is very different from the kind used in following rules known as algorithms. For example, to solve a problem such as

$$\begin{array}{r} 46 \\ + 46 \\ \hline \end{array}$$

children are usually told where to write 2, where to write 1, and so forth. I do not give them such rules, and children invent their own ways of writing that serve as tools for thinking.

These ideas were confirmed in May of one school year. Connie Kamii told me that the third graders receiving traditional instruction were being taught rules of writing to get answers to problems such as

$$2\,\overline{)84} \qquad \text{and} \qquad 3\,\overline{)93}$$

I decided to find out how my second graders approached these problems and asked, "How would you divide 84 by 2?" In no time, at least a third of the class had the answer, with an explanation: "Half of 80 is 40, and half of 4 is 2, so the answer is 42." For 93 divided by 3, they had the same kind of argument: "Ninety is 3 times 30, and 3 is 3 times 1, so the answer is 31." Children who have not been made to follow rules of writing do their own thinking and do not become dependent on adults or on paper and pencil.

CHAPTER 7

The Use of Situations in Daily Living and Other Activities

by Linda Joseph

A constructivist math program cannot be limited to only the math hour, for two reasons. First, arithmetic is what children construct out of their real-life experiences, and not something that is put into their heads from textbooks. Second, teachers cannot turn children's mental activity on only during the math hour. If we want mentally active children during the math hour, we have to encourage them to put things into relationships and to be alert and curious throughout the day.

A constructivist teacher is constantly on the lookout for situations that can be used to develop children's numerical thinking. Some of these situations appear in daily, weekly, or monthly routines, such as taking attendance and lunch counts. Others appear fortuitously, as when a child says, "I have an odd number of holes [eyelets] on the sides of my shoe, but, when I lace it, it comes out even!" A third kind of activity, such as cooking, is a real-life activity that naturally occurs in children's lives but has to be planned by the teacher to happen in the classroom. In this chapter, I will give examples of each of these three types of activities.

DAILY, WEEKLY, AND MONTHLY ROUTINES

Taking Attendance, Ordering Lunches, and Counting Lunch Money

Each morning upon entering the classroom, the children in my class perform a simple procedure that simultaneously creates an attendance record and records their choices for lunch. The children each have an assigned number from 1 to about 26 (depending on the class size) that corresponds to the class register, which is in alphabetical order. These numbers are written on small cards that are hanging on individual hooks on a bulletin board near the entryway to the classroom. Another part of the bulletin board is divided into three sections with three labels: "Regular lunch," "Soup," and "Brought lunch." Under each of these labels are four rows of five pins. The children each take the tag with their assigned number and hang it on a pin under the appropriate label. As class begins, I ask, "How many regular lunches are we ordering today? How many soups? How many brought lunches?" and the children give me a tally for each item. The next question, "Is anyone absent?" is answered by a glance to see if any tags are still hanging in their original positions. The children add together the three numbers for lunches and any absences, to make sure the whole class has been accounted for.

After recording the lunch money received from individual children, I invite two or three to add the total amount collected each morning. The children separate the money into checks, dollar bills, and coins and count it all in their heads in a way that surprised me at the beginning. Going through the checks, they usually add only the dollar amounts first. Then they add the bills and take care of all the dollars. The next step is to combine the coins and the cents on the checks in some way that results in making dollars. They end by counting the leftover coins.

The following is an example. The money collected included four checks, for $3.40, $4.25, $3.40, and $4.25; five dollar bills; four quarters; six dimes; and three nickels. One child found $14 altogether on the checks, added to this the dollar bills and got $19, and added the four quarters and got $20. He then counted the dimes and nickels and found 75¢, put it with 25¢ on one of the checks, and announced, "That's 21 dollars." He then added the cents on the other three checks, found the total to be $1.05, and declared that the whole thing came to $22.05. I used to think that paper and pencil were indispensable for this chore until I saw the ingenuity of these second graders!

If children get different totals, those disagreeing with each other get together and start all over until they come to an agreement.

Some children are not willing to try counting money at the beginning of the year. Most, however, do become interested by the end of the year.

Recording Time for Trips to the Bathroom

To encourage children to tell time, I post a sign-out sheet near the door, for recording bathroom visits. My rule is that two boys and two girls can go at one time. Each child going to the bathroom is asked to record the time he or she leaves the room and the time of return.

The children often check each other with comments such as, "You can't put 11:30 because it's not even 11 o'clock yet." The other may say, "Oh, it's 10:30!" I used to smile with curiosity when I saw a child pause by the sheet with pencil in hand, eyes raised to the clock. Then I saw that it was 8:59 and realized that he was waiting for one more click so he could accurately and confidently record 9:00.

Voting

The children call for a vote for everything from choosing games to deciding whether to go outdoors or stay inside and play. The class at one time often voted to choose between their two favorite whole-class games: Around the World (described in Chapter 6) and Tic-Tac-15 (described in Chapter 8). This was so often a topic of debate that they decided to play the two games on alternate Wednesdays.

In voting, the children found that there was no need to count the opposing votes when there were only two choices. As long as the first group was more or less than half the class, they accurately proclaimed the winner.

Going to the Media Center

We have an open media center, which means children can go at any time to check out books or to do their prescriptions (in which I prescribe a particular center or topic of research, or the use of computers). Since there is a limit of two children per prescribed activity (my rule), the children know that only six can go at a time for prescriptions. They, therefore, frequently make a quick count of the number of children remaining in the classroom and deduce whether or not they can go.

Changing the Calendar

When one month ends and it is time to take off the old dates and put the new ones on the large calendar (a grid that has only the days of the week at the top), the children ask to help. To take advantage of their interest, the changing of the calendar is made into a large-group activity. I ask the children on what day of the week the new month will begin. Some have learned to predict the day of the week the following month will begin, before all the numbers have been replaced. One child's procedure for doing this was to count down 4 weeks from the first of the new month, a leap of 29 days ($4 \times 7 + 1$), and then add either 1 or 2 days, depending on how many days are in the month. She then knew the last day of the coming month and deduced the first day of the following month.

Ensuring That Game Pieces Are Not Lost

The children are responsible for making sure all game pieces are accounted for. Before each game, the groups count to see if all the pieces are there. At the end of the game, they again count to be sure all the pieces are put back. Small pieces often fall to the floor and would be lost if there were no count. The children know that they should immediately alert the rest of the class if parts cannot be found. They say, "There are only 48 cards here. That means 4 are missing," or "There are two red and two yellow pieces missing from *Parcheesi*. Here's one; so we have to find three."

Dealing with Overdue Books and Fines

Once a month, a list is received from the media center concerning overdue books and fines. This list is posted near the door as a reminder, and the children often read it while lining up to leave the classroom. Sometimes someone remarks, "Wow, Becky, you owe 75 cents and 45 cents. That's over a dollar. You need to return two more books, too." Others crowd around and begin adding their amounts of overdue fines. A few return to their desks and write their totals down to take home.

Paying for School Supplies

We are permitted to sell pencils, paper, and other school supplies in the classroom, to save trips to the office. This gives the children a chance to work with real money. The buyer and seller have to agree on the amount bought.

When children need pencils or paper but have not brought any money, they are permitted to charge. They sign their names on a sheet of paper, along with the date, the items bought, and the amount charged. Periodically, the children add up the totals of each person's charges. One such example was, "Peter, you owe 15 cents and 50 cents." Another child said, "That's 65 cents." and Peter retorted, "That's 15 cents and 50 cents!"

One morning, we had almost no supplies left, and I sent Becky to the office to replenish our stock of pencils by getting five of each kind available. When she returned, the class was curious as to how many and what kinds of pencils she had. I asked them to figure this out by telling them that she had five of each kind and by asking Becky how many different kinds she had brought back. She announced, "I got four different designs." The classmates began chattering among themselves saying, "That's 4 fives," or "That's 5 times 4." Several asked, "Do you have 20 pencils?" They then crowded around, separating the pencils into four groups of five pencils to prove their answer, some commenting, "I got it right."

Paying for Popsicles on Birthdays

Parents often buy popsicles (25¢ each) for the entire class, to celebrate their child's birthday. With a blank check to be filled in, the children eagerly begin determining how much money is needed. Some children touch each desk, walking around the room, saying, "Twenty-five and 25 is 50; 25 and 25 is another 50; so that's a dollar," and continue in this manner. Others look at the tags on the lunch board and count, "One, two, three, four, That's a dollar." Others write down 25¢ many times, one for each child, then count four numbers and place a 1 beside each group, until all twenty-fives are accounted for. If there is a disagreement, they start again, counting carefully.

Adding Numbers of Soup Labels

The Campbell Soup Company gives equipment to schools that collect large numbers of soup labels, and at our school the class that has the highest number at the end of the collection period is treated to an ice-skating party. An enormous chart on the lunchroom wall has the names of all the teachers down the left side and the months across the top, so that the number of soup labels collected by each class can be recorded at the end of each month.

At the end of September, the children were delighted to be able to compare totals from class to class. At the end of October, the totals posted held a nice surprise: Our class had the highest total for that month. After seeing that, some children began adding the two monthly totals for every class. This ranged from 11 for one kindergarten class to over 400 for our own second-grade class. When they began adding the numbers for third grade, they found that one class had over 600 labels.

Each month thereafter, at least five children excused themselves from games to add soup label totals and to return with their findings. I still marvel at these children's ability to add big numbers in their heads and to write only the totals in the thousands. Of the many visits to the lunchroom chart, only one child ever chose to waste time, and the others decided to send him back to class.

FORTUITOUS SITUATIONS

In addition to using routine situations that come up in the life of a second-grade class, I also make math lessons by picking up on children's spontaneous remarks. These remarks are important because they spring from the depth of children's thinking. The child's observation about the eyelets on his tennis shoes in this section is an example that had not occurred to me. It is also frequently the case that, if an idea intrigues one child, it will intrigue others who are at the same developmental level.

The following two activities sprang from spontaneous remarks that had too much potential to ignore until the next math period.

Pizzas

We were treated to a pizza party by a local pizzeria, for winning a contest. When the boxes containing the pizzas arrived, I decided to spice the event up with a little arithmetic. I informed the class that each of the four pizzas would serve half the class. Someone immediately said, "That means there are 12 slices in each one, because we have 24 here today." I then asked, "How many slices are there in all four boxes?" One of the quietest children raised his hand and confidently said, "Four times 12 is 48 because 12 plus 12 is 24 and 2 twenty-fours is 48."

Tennis Shoes

As mentioned earlier, one day, just before our math period, Jerry commented, "I have an odd number of holes [eyelets] on the sides of my shoe, but, when I lace it, it comes out even!" When I asked the class if they had odd or even numbers of eyelets on their shoes, many children admitted to not knowing what odd and even meant. I asked Jerry if he could explain, and he gave the following lecture.

He wrote the numerals 1 through 10 on the chalkboard, in a column, and drew the appropriate number of circles beside each one. He then drew a ring around each pair of circles (see Figure 7.1). When he finished, he said, "Every time you see a circle without a partner, he's the odd man out. That makes the number odd."

When everybody knew what we were talking about, all the children wearing tennis shoes began counting their shoes' eyelets, to determine whether they had odd or even numbers of holes. They had no need for further directions as they began milling about making their own analyses. They were delighted to find that not only did odd plus odd make an even number, but that two shoes or four odds were even as well.

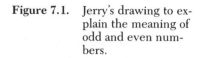 **Figure 7.1.** Jerry's drawing to explain the meaning of odd and even numbers.

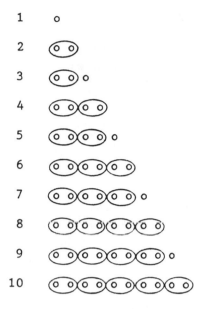

Since not all children were wearing lace-up type shoes, they asked to repeat the activity the next day, when they would wear that kind of shoe. So on the following day, I asked each child to write on a card the number of holes in her or his shoes and then to choose a partner. The pairs of children mentally added the numbers written on their card and checked their answers by physically counting the holes. Each couple then joined another couple and added the number of holes in all four pairs of shoes. They found that, no matter how many pairs of evens and odds were added, they always ended with an even number.

TEACHER-PLANNED ACTIVITIES

The preceding two categories of activities were about situations that did not originate during the math hour. This third category consists of activities planned for the math period. While I generally spend half of the math period on the kind of discussions described in Chapter 6 and the other half on games, I sometimes introduce other types of activities such as cooking and making parachutes. The reason for this must be obvious: Variety stimulates mental activity and pushes the frontiers of our thinking.

I begin here with two cooking activities, then go to an estimation activity using M&M candies, and end with the physics of parachutes.

S'mores

A s'more is a graham cracker sandwich baked in an oven until the chocolate and six marshmallows in it melt. My student teacher told the class
that *they* had to figure out all the amounts that would be needed. She
formed three groups and asked one to decide how many boxes of crackers
were needed, another to figure out how many chocolate bars had to be
bought, and a third to calculate whether one bag of miniature marshmallows was enough for everyone.

The student teacher handed a bag of miniature marshmallows to the
marshmallow group and instructed them to find out how many were in
the bag and if that was enough for everyone to have six each. However,
she asked them to estimate the number first, and some of their answers
were 250, 150, 450, 199, 200, 660, and 312. Instead of estimating, however, Eric quickly figured out that 144 marshmallows were needed because "Twenty-four people times 3 marshmallows is 72, and if there are 6
per person, that's twice as many, and 72 plus 72 is 144." The children then
began counting and found 636 in the bag.

Meanwhile, the student teacher told the chocolate-bar group that each
bar had enough for four people. The children added 4 several times (4,
8, 12, and so on) and when they reached 24, they declared that they
needed six bars of chocolate.

The graham-cracker group was a disaster. They had too many factors to
contend with: Did one cracker make one s'more or two, since each
cracker was to be broken in half? The fact that there were three packages
in a box further confused them. The children physically broke each
cracker into two pieces to see the top and the bottom and to count them
as one s'more. They had to break and count all three packages, rather
than use one package and triple it.

The following day the student teacher announced, "This is what you
told me to buy yesterday. We'll throw out this box of crackers and open a
new one. Let's count a package."[1]

Led by the student teacher, the class found 11 crackers in a package.
Another package was counted, and again 11 were found. Finally, someone
announced, "Eleven and 11 is 22! One box is enough because 22 and 11
is 33."

After distributing the crackers, marshmallows, and chocolate, the children assembled their ingredients. One asked, "How will we know which

---

[1] I would have preferred postponing the activity until the *children* figured out all the
necessary quantities themselves. Adults often solve problems for children, thereby depriving them of opportunities to think.

is whose?" Amy solved that problem by drawing a 3 × 4 grid on the chalkboard, duplicating the arrangement of the cookies on the baking sheet. After placing their cookies on the pan, the children reported to Amy, who recorded their class identification numbers in the corresponding spots.

Some children volunteered to be clock watchers, and I asked, "What time is it?" and "What time will it be in 3 minutes?"

"They are growing!" one child remarked. This was a good opportunity to teach the word *expanding* and to ask if someone could think of something else that expanded while cooking.

Doughnuts

Another cooking activity was perfect for graphing. The student teacher began by telling the class that we were going to make doughnuts using cans of refrigerator biscuit dough. As usual, she asked the pupils how many cans would be needed if there were 10 biscuits in each can. She then asked each child to decide which one of four colors they preferred for their glaze: red, blue, green, or yellow. Their replies were written on the board. Blue was favored by 14, yellow was chosen by 5, green by 3, and red by 2.

The student teacher then asked the children to draw a picture or make a graph to show how much glaze we needed for each color. Some made vertical or horizontal bar-type graphs. I was surprised by the large variety of products, samples of which are shown in Figure 7.2. There were three main categories. More than half of the children made graphs of some kind (Figure 7.2a) while 29% represented discrete quantities without equal units on a line (Figure 7.2b) and 14% represented continuous quantities (Figure 7.2c). We had done one graphing activity earlier in the year, and I could see that the children had benefited from it only if they were already at a certain developmental level.

M&M Candies

I brought out a 1-pound bag of M&M candies one day and poured the contents into a clear container, asking for estimations of the number the bag had held. This would have worked better by secret ballot, because the children were influenced by each other's comments of "too high" or "too low." Most guessed less than 100, with the average guess of about 50. The child with the highest guess, of 200, was told that that many would have burst the bag.

When I asked for a quick and easy way to count the candy, one child

Figure 7.2.   Three categories of response to the teacher's request for a picture
or graph to represent the class's color preferences.

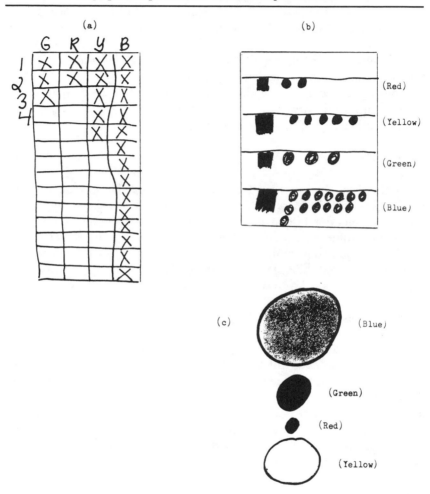

said, "By tens," and another said, "By fives." They voted and decided to
count by tens. When we reached 100 with nearly a full bowl left to go,
they couldn't believe there could be another hundred. When we reached
200, they couldn't imagine having another hundred left. When we
reached 400, with a dwindling number left in the bowl, they erroneously
started saying that there were probably at least 600 or 700.

As each group of 10 tens was counted, the children put a circle of yarn
around it, at my suggestion. Glancing into the bowl, which was nearly
empty, I silently took over, finished arranging the remaining candy into

two lines of 10, with 6 loose candies in another. I then asked each child to come up and count the entire amount silently and to write his or her answer on paper. Most did this effortlessly, and then compared answers. They finally agreed on a total of 426 candies. One interesting note was the fact that, even though yarn was encircling each group of 100, most children counted as though the yarn were not there. The children counted by tens, which was what they had voted for in the first place. The organization of their counting by tens reminded me of Sharon Ross's 1986 study with lima beans (see Chapter 2).

I then asked, "If each person wanted to eat 10 candies, how many would we have to have, and would there be enough?" The solution took many forms, from counting people by tens to repeatedly writing down the number 10.

I then asked if we had enough for us to have 20 each. This was much more difficult to figure, and we ran out of time, with only one child giving a response of, "If we need 250 for us to get 10 each, then we'd have to add another 250 for us to get another 10 each, and that's 500; so we don't have enough." Several could see her reasoning and nodded in agreement.

The M&Ms were handy for math problems in subsequent lessons. For example, I asked, "If there are 60 left, how many would these two children get?" The class was able to tell me quickly, "Thirty, because 30 and 30 is 60." When I asked them to split the candies among three people, they could also mentally make three groups, telling me to count by twos and change it to 20 each. Next, I asked them to divide the 60 candies among four, and in a few moments they had again figured it out mentally. When I asked how they knew, one said he just took 5 candies from each of the other three groups and gave those 15 to the fourth person, and that left the first three people with 15, too. Amazed at their thinking, I said, "Well, do you think five people can share the candies equally?" The children again had the answer in just a few moments, without using paper and pencil. Half the class could do this problem; yet I have never seen a problem of this type in our current traditional second-grade mathematics textbooks.

Parachutes

I conclude with an activity that combines physics and mathematics— or measurement, to be more exact. As stated in *Physical Knowledge in Preschool Education* (Kamii & DeVries, 1978), young children think hard when they act on objects, can see the objects' reactions, and can vary their actions.

Our objectives for the day were to study children's methods of measurement, to observe how the children worked, and to review terms such as *circle, square,* and *rectangle.* I displayed plastic garbage bags, string, yardsticks, and rulers and told the children that they were going to design their own parachutes. Most of them decided to make rectangular or square ones. They paired themselves and began working eagerly. (Whenever possible, I ask children to work in pairs, to maximize both social interaction and independent work.) The yardstick or ruler was occasionally used, but only to make straight lines. As for the string, the children simply unwound a desired length and used it as a standard for the other pieces.

When all in the class had finished making their parachutes, I took them in small groups to the gymnasium, where we have a balcony on the second floor, to test how well their products worked. At their countdown, they let go and watched their creations drift to the floor. When I asked, "Whose won?" they indicated that the winner was the last one to touch the floor. Each subsequent group had a similar response.

After these empirical tests, I asked what it was that made a good parachute. The pupils looked blank for a moment until one said, "Sam made a good one." When questioned why his was good, they said, "Because it was slow coming down." When asked why his went slowly, Sherry replied, "I don't know, but his also went straighter." Sam said, "That's because Cary said to put a hole in the middle." Nearly everyone then cut a hole in the middle of theirs and began taking turns climbing on a stool to see if a hole helped control the direction.

At the end of the hour, I told the class, "You've had a day to experiment. Tomorrow, you and your partner are going to make two more parachutes. Make them alike in some ways and different in some ways. Try to figure out what makes a parachute better." The class had caught on quickly; most parachutes were designed like Sam's the next day, with a hole in the top.

These three kinds of activities, some routine, some accidental, and some planned, all have a place in the classroom. The children experiencing math activities in their day-to-day living show their fondness for it when they exclaim, "We could do math all day!"

CHAPTER 8

Group Games

with Linda Joseph

Games can be used in ways that foster or hinder the development of autonomy. Since autonomy as the goal of education is a primary focus of the math instruction in our Hall-Kent classrooms, we have given a good deal of thought to the ways commercially available and teacher-created games can be used to stimulate and develop children's ability to think independently as they engage in the process of constructing logico-mathematical knowledge. This chapter will introduce readers to some of the games that we have used most successfully with second graders. In addition to the suggestions given here, more detailed information on principles of teaching, including how to introduce games in ways that promote the development of autonomy, can be found in *Young Children Reinvent Arithmetic* (Kamii, 1985, Chapter 8).

Games are difficult to classify because many (such as Four-in-a-Row, discussed later) can be used for addition or subtraction, and they can be made easy or hard depending on the numbers used. We have organized them into four main categories: games involving addition, those involving premultiplication (repeated addition), those involving subtraction, and others. We hope readers will consider each one for possible modification.

Three points need to be mentioned about the descriptions of specific games: (1) When the number of players is not specified, this means that the number can vary from two to four. (2) Complete source information about the games identified as commercially made is given in the Appendix at the back of the book, as are some of the mail-order firms from which games may be purchased. (3) We never specify how the first player is to be chosen, and not all the details of each game are spelled out. The reason for this omission is that, for the development of children's autonomy, it is good that they have to make their own decisions. When we define cognitive objectives in the context of autonomy as the broad goal, we use math games for children's socio-moral development as well as for their construction of logico-mathematical knowledge.

Games Involving Addition

BASIC GAMES

We single out certain games for later presentation because they offer advantages that many teachers prefer to consider separately. Those are board games using dice, games involving physical-knowledge activities, and games involving money. The games described here are organized generally in order of difficulty, from those requiring the players to make 10 with two numbers to those involving much larger sums.

Making 10 with Two Numbers

Of the four games in this group, the first two are easier because they can be played by trial and error. In the last two games, the players have to know what numbers to look for or ask for.

FIND 10

Materials: Home-made numeral cards, six each of numbers 1 through 9 (54 cards); alternatively, playing cards, ace through 9. Ace represents 1.

Play: The object of the game is to find two cards that make a total of 10 (8 + 2, for example). The person who collects more pairs than anybody else is the winner.

All the cards are dealt. Each player keeps the cards dealt to him[1] in a face-down stack, without looking at them.

When his turn comes, each person turns over the top card of his stack. If this card can be used with one on the table (placed there before the first player begins) to make a total of 10, the player can take it and keep the pair. If there are no cards that can be used, he has to discard his card in the middle of the table, face up. For example, if he turns over a 6 and there is no 4 on the table, the player has to discard the 6, and the turn passes to the next player.

---

[1]To avoid frequent use of the somewhat awkward "his or her" and similar paired constructions, in these game descriptions the use of single gender-specific pronouns will be alternated. Thus, the pronoun used is not meant to convey any assumptions about the gender of the players.

DRAW 10

Number of Players: Four.

Materials: Home-made numeral cards, six each of numbers 1 through 9 (54 cards); alternatively, playing cards, ace through 9. Ace represents 1.

Play: One card is drawn from the deck and is set aside throughout the game, so that there will be an odd card without a mate at the end of the game. All the other cards are dealt.

Each player goes through the cards received trying to find pairs that make 10 (6 + 4, for example). All the pairs thus made are discarded in the middle of the table.

The players then take turns, each holding her cards like a fan and letting the person to her left draw one of them without looking at them. If the person who draws the card can use it to make 10 with one of the cards in her hand, she discards the pair in the middle of the table. If she cannot use it, she has to keep it. She then holds all her cards like a fan so that the person to her left can draw one of them by chance.

Play continues until one person is left holding the odd card and loses the game.

TENS CONCENTRATION

Materials: Home-made numeral cards, six each of numbers 1 through 9 (54 cards); alternatively, playing cards, ace through 9. Ace represents 1.

Play: Sixteen cards are placed in the middle of the table, face down, in a 4 × 4 arrangement. The players take turns turning over two cards, trying to turn up a pair that totals 10 (a 7 and a 3, for example). If a pair can be made, the player keeps it and continues to play as long as he is successful. If he is not successful, he returns the two cards to their original face-down positions and replaces any cards he took with new ones from the deck.

With 16 face-down cards on the table, the turn passes to the next player to the left.

The person who collects the greatest number of pairs is the winner.

This game can be varied by increasing the number of cards placed on the table. A 5 × 5 or 6 × 6 arrangement may be more interesting.

GO 10

Number of Players: Three or four. (A two-player game has its advantages and disadvantages)

Materials: Home-made numeral cards, six each of numbers 1 through 9 (54 cards); alternatively, playing cards, ace through 9. Ace represents 1.

Play: The object of the game is to make 10 with two cards (a 9 and a 1, for example). All the cards are dealt. The players ask specific people for specific cards in a way similar to the card game Go Fish. For example, John may say to Carol, "Do you have a 1?" If Carol has a 1, she has to give it up to John. John then lays this 1 and a 9 in front of himself, face up.

A player can continue asking for a card as long as he gets the card he requested. If he does not get the card he asked for, the turn passes to the person who said, "I don't have it." (Alternatively, the players can take turns in a clockwise direction.)

The person who makes the greatest number of pairs is the winner.

Making 10 with Four Numbers

TAKE TEN

Materials: A commercially made board game shown in Photograph 8.1. There are 66 round cards bearing the numerals 1 through 7, in the following quantities:

1 – 22 cards	5 – 4 cards
2 – 16 cards	6 – 2 cards
3 – 12 cards	7 – 2 cards
4 – 7 cards	Joker – 1 card

Play: The object of the game is to make 10 with four cards in a row, horizontally, vertically, or diagonally.

All the cards are placed face down in the box, and each player takes three cards. Each in turn places a card on any one of the circles on the board. She then replaces this card with one from the box, so that she will have three cards again.

When a player completes a row of four cards that make 10, she collects the four cards. The Joker can be used for any value. (The child in Photo-

Wayne Hamby

Photograph 8.1.   *Take Ten*

graph 8.1 knew that his opponent was holding the Joker, and so chose to block his opponent from completing a row.)

The player who collects the most cards is the winner.

Making Sums Up to 12 with Two or More Numbers

SHUT THE BOX

Materials: Nine cards numbered 1 through 9; two dice; paper and pencil for scorekeeping.

This game is commercially made (see Appendix), but other versions have existed for a long time. The version with cards and dice is described here for those who do not have access to the commercial game. While the commercial game is not essential, it is desirable for two reasons: (1) Children enjoy manipulating its plastic flaps much more than cards and (2) it has a slide indicator for recording a player's score.

Play: The nine cards are arranged in a line in sequence from 1 to 9, face up. Each player in turn rolls both dice and turns over as many cards as she wishes, to make the total of the dice. For example, if she rolls a 6 and a 2, she can turn over the 8; the 1 and the 7; the 2 and the 6; the 3 and the 5; or the 1, the 2, and the 5.

She rolls the dice again and keeps playing until she cannot make a total with the remaining cards. She then totals the number of points left on the cards remaining face up and records it. The turn passes to the next player, who begins with all nine cards, as before.

The points left at the end of each turn are added to the player's previous total. When a player reaches 45 points, she is eliminated. The winner is the last person to reach 45 points.

On the slide indicator for recording the player's score, there are 45 notches in a line to indicate points from 0 through 45. These are numbered in multiples of 5 (5, 10, 15, 20, and so on). Children, therefore, have to figure out where to place the indicator when their score is not a multiple of 5.

ALWAYS 12

Materials: Seventy-two round cards bearing the numbers 0 through 6 in the following quantities:

0 – 8 cards	4 – 12 cards
1 – 10 cards	5 – 8 cards
2 – 12 cards	6 – 8 cards
3 – 14 cards	

Also needed is a stand that holds four stacks of cards or a sheet of paper creased to show four sections, on which four stacks of cards can be made.

This commercially made game, called *Toujours 12* in French, is not available in the United States. However, it can easily be made at home.

Play: The object of the game is to make a total of 12 with four cards.

All the cards are scattered, face down, in the box. Each person takes three cards. In turn, each player places a card on a quadrant of the stand or creased paper and then takes a card from the box to have three cards in his hand again. Empty quadrants must be filled before cards can be placed atop one another. (See Figure 8.1 for several examples of this process.) The person who makes a total of 12 with four cards can take these four cards (see Figure 8.1a).

Figure 8.1b already has a total of 12. If the next player puts a 0 in the empty space, he can take the four cards (Figure 8.1c). If he has only fives, he is forced to make a total of 17 (Figure 8.1d). If the next person puts a 1 on the 6 (Figure 8.1e), he makes a total of 12 and can take the four cards. The 6 underneath his 1 would be left for the next round, as would any other cards that had been underneath his other collected cards.

The person who gets the most cards is the winner.

Figure 8.1. *Always 12.*

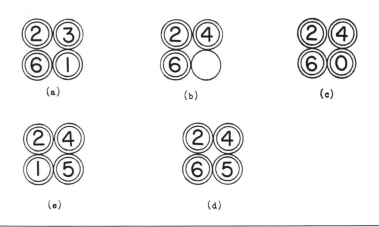

(a)   (b)   (c)

(e)   (d)

EVEN DOMINOES

Material: Dominoes.

Play: This is a game invented by children in Linda's class. The object of the game is to make points by making even-numbered combinations.

All the dominoes are turned face down. The players draw five dominoes each. One domino from the pile is placed on the table. The players take turns placing a domino so that the two touching ends (not the outer ends) make an even number. For example, if a 6–3 domino is on the table, the next player can play either 0, 2, 4, or 6 on the 6 end; or a 1, 3, or 5 on the 3 end, since those combinations make even numbers. After each turn, the players draw another domino so that they always have five. A player's score is the total made with the two touching ends.

The first player to reach 70 wins. In another version, the players continue to play until all the dominoes are played; the highest score wins.

Making Sums Up to 15 with Two or More Numbers

QUINCE

Materials: Playing cards from ace through 10 (ace = 1); 10 bottlecaps or buttons for each player.

Play: The object of the game is to get as close to a total of 15 as possible without going over it.

The dealer deals two cards to each player, including herself, one at a time, face down. Each player looks at her cards without letting the others see them. The player to the dealer's left begins play. If her cards add up to less than 15, she may ask the dealer for another card, hoping to get one that will bring her total closer to 15. In turn, the other players, too, may ask for another card if they want to. A player may keep asking for another card every time her turn comes, until she is satisfied with her total and says "I stand pat"; or until she goes over 15 and is out of the game.

For example, in a two-player game, one receives a 6 and an ace. He knows that 6 + 1 is too low to win; so he asks the dealer for another card. If he receives a 2, he has only 9 points.

The dealer has a 9 and a 3. She could stop here but decides to ask for a card. If she gets a 5, she goes over 15 and is out, and the other player automatically wins the round and gets a bottlecap.

If there are more than two players, all the totals are compared when all the players have finished asking for cards.

The player who has the highest total without going over 15 is the winner of the round and gets a bottlecap. In case of a tie, there is no winner for the round.

The winner of the game is the person to collect the most bottlecaps, or the first person to collect 10 bottlecaps.

TIC-TAC-15

Number of Players: Two (or two teams)

Materials: Paper and pencil (or a chalkboard and chalk).

Play: This is an excellent team game that Linda's class regularly plays with great excitement.

A Tic-Tac-Toe grid is drawn, and the children take turns writing numbers in the spaces. The object of the game is to make a total of 15 with three numbers in a vertical, horizontal, or diagonal line.

There are two ways to choose the numbers that can be used by each player. One way is for one player to use the even numbers (2, 4, 6, 8, and 10) and for the other to use the odd numbers (1, 3, 5, 7, and 9). In this game each number can be used only once. Another way of assigning the numbers is by using 10 cards numbered 1 through 10. The players (or teams) take turns drawing a card.

As variations, the total can be changed to 16, 20, or any other number, and the children can experiment with the numbers that can be used.

Making 20 with Two or More Numbers

TWENTY-TWENTY

Materials: Deck of playing cards from ace through 10 (40 cards with the face cards removed); 24 bottlecaps or small tiles marked with the number 20. The tiles are either bathroom tiles bought at a color tiles store or plastic blank tiles called Color Tiles (Cuisenaire catalog).

Play: Each player takes six bottlecaps and is dealt five cards. The players take turns putting one card down at a time next to one that is already on the table (see Figure 8.2). After putting down a card, each player takes the top card of the deck so that he will have five cards again.

When a player puts down a card that makes a total of 20, either vertically or horizontally, he closes the line with two bottlecaps or tiles, as shown in Figure 8.2. The person who uses up his six tiles first is the winner.

TENS AND TWENTIES

Materials: Forty-eight sturdy plastic triangles, with numbers as shown in Figure 8.3, which come in this commercially made game. The triangles come in two sets. One set has red lines separating the numbers, which range from 0 to 10. The second set has green lines separating the numbers 0 to 20 (see Appendix).

Play: The two sets may be used separately as two games or mixed together. The triangles are shuffled, face down, and divided equally among

Figure 8.2. Twenty-Twenty.

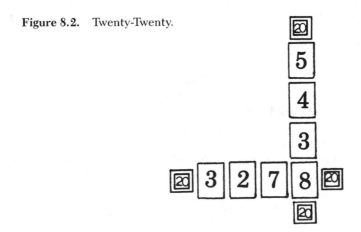

Figure 8.3. *Tens and Twenties.*

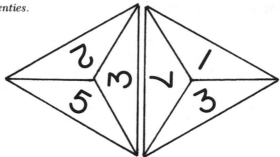

all the players. The first player puts down any triangle of her choice. In turn, each player then puts down a triangle in such a way that the numbers linked make a total of 10, if only the red set is used, or a total of 10 or 20, if both sets are used. Figure 8.3 shows an example of such a link.

The person who has used up all her triangles first is the winner. A player who does not have any triangle to play must pass.

A challenging version is to play alone so that each set of 24 triangles forms a hexagon with all the numbers correctly linked.

Making Sums Up to 21 with Two or More Numbers

BLACK JACK

Materials: Deck of 52 cards with the following values: 2 through 10 are worth the values shown, the face cards are each worth 10, and aces are worth 1 or 11. Ten bottlecaps or blocks.

Play: This game is played just like Quince, except that the players try not to go over 21. The winner is the person to collect the most bottlecaps.

Making Sums Up to 30

BUTTERFLY

Materials: Forty playing cards, ace through 10.

Play: Each player is dealt three cards, which remain face up in front of him throughout the game. Seven other cards are turned face up and shown in a line in the middle of the table. The rest of the cards make up the drawing pile.

When his turn comes, each player picks up as many cards from the middle as necessary to make the same total as that of his three cards.

When he cannot make any more sets of the same total, the cards that he took are replaced with cards from the drawing pile, so that there will be seven cards for the next player.

The person who has the most sets at the end is the winner.

FOUR-IN-A-ROW

Number of Players: Two.

Materials: A board such as that shown in Figure 8.4; 2 small rings; 24 tiles or buttons, 12 each of two colors.

Play: Each player takes all the buttons of one color. Each in turn chooses two numbers on the small square, places the rings on these numbers, finds the sum on the large square, and covers it with one of her tiles. The object of the game is to be first to make a row of four with one's tiles, vertically, horizontally, or diagonally. If a sum is already covered, the player wastes a turn.[2]

Variations: This game can be made much harder by using larger addends in the small square and changing the game to Five-in-a-Row. Each player gets 15 tiles in Five-in-a-Row, which is shown in Figure 8.5, and in the following two other variations.

With addends of 37, 15, 17, 29, 19, 8, 45, 27, and 26 in the small square, the large square consists of the following numbers: 48, 66, 36, 60, 64, 43, 34, 72, 46, 34, 56, 82, 63, 37, 45, 44, 71, 42, 35, 42, 27, 74, 62, 23, 45, 32, 44, 53, 46, 42, 54, 25, 52, 56, 41, and 55.

With addends of 55, 22, 28, 42, 11, 37, 33, 19, and 45 in the small square, the large square consists of 83, 50, 64, 79, 77, 61, 92, 74, 33, 41, 52, 30, 70, 75, 88, 97, 59, 53, 48, 44, 61, 78, 87, 39, 47, 66, 64, 56, 65, 82, 70, 56, 67, 55, 73, and 100.

Making Sums Greater Than 30

KNOCK-KNOCK

Materials: Deck of 52 cards with the following values: ace is worth 1, 2 through 10 are worth the values shown, and the face cards are each worth 10 points.

---

[2]Credit goes to Grayson Wheatley, of Florida State University, and to Paul Cobb and his colleagues at Purdue University for introducing this game and its variations to us.

Figure 8.4. Four-in-a-Row.

5	6	7
8	9	10
11	12	13

16	19	22	14	17
24	11	15	20	21
15	23	18	12	19
25	20	21	17	22
13	14	23	16	18

Figure 8.5. Five-in-a-Row.

15	19	12
23	17	32
51	11	14

34	27	38	32	47	66
26	29	31	42	36	51
70	30	33	35	29	44
63	23	26	40	55	74
34	37	49	68	28	31
83	43	46	62	65	25

Play: Each player is dealt four cards, and the remaining cards make up the drawing pile. The players take turns taking the top card of the drawing pile and discarding one of the five cards that are in their hands. The object of the game is to make the largest total value possible (or the smallest).

When a player thinks he has the largest total, he says, "Knock-knock," and everybody else has one more turn. All the players then add their totals.

LINEUP

Materials: Fifty-eight tiles bearing the following numbers: 1 through 10 (five of each, totaling 50 tiles); -5 and -10 (four of each, totaling 8 tiles).

Play: Each player takes a -5 and a -10 tile first. All the other tiles are then scattered on the table, face down, and each player takes five of them, for a total of seven. One tile is then turned over and placed in the middle of the table.

The players take turns adding a tile to the original tile, forming a line, and the object of the game is to be the one who makes exactly 45 points. For example, if the first tile is a 7 and the players in turn put down a 10, a 3, a 10, and an 8, the next player can win the round if she has a 7. After putting a tile down, each player replaces it with one of the face-down tiles so that she will have seven tiles again.

A player who goes over 45 points loses the game and is out. The -5 and -10 tiles can be played at any time, but players learn to keep them to use them advantageously when they are in danger of going over 45 points.

Tally marks or objects can be used to keep track of the number of rounds won. However, our children simply go on to the next round without further ado.

DOMINIQUE OR DOMICOLOR

Materials: Forty-four cards—*Dominique*; 48 cards—*Domicolor* (although more attractive and sturdier, not available in the United States); four stands that hold three cards each; two pegboards and six pegs (in Educational Teaching aids catalog; see Appendix); or paper and pencil for scorekeeping (see Photograph 8.2).

The cards for this commercially made game can be made at home by buying lightweight cardboard at an art supply store and having it cut into 44 pieces (6.9 cm × 2.3 cm). Also needed are a package of ¾-inch diameter self-adhesive circles in assorted colors, preferably red, yellow,

Photograph 8.2. *Dominique* or *Domicolor*

blue, and green (Dennison No. 43-851); and Scotch tape to put on both sides of the cards to protect them from wear.

Three colored circles are placed on each card, 2 mm from the edges and 4 mm apart. Eight of the cards should have three circles of the same color: two all-green (G), two all-yellow (Y), two all-red (R), and two all-blue (B) cards. The other 36 cards should have circles of various combinations of two or three different colors, as follows:

BBG	BBY	BBR	GGB	GGY	GGR	YYG	YYB	YYR
RRB	RRG	RRY	GBG	GYG	GRG	BGB	BYB	BRB
YGY	YBY	YRY	RGR	RBR	RYR	GBY	GYB	GBR
GRB	GYR	GRY	BGR	BGY	BYR	BRY	YGR	YBR

This is the composition for *Dominique*, the 44-card game, which is the one focused on here.

Play: The object of the game is to win the greatest number of points by making lines of three or more circles of the same color.

All the cards are mixed, face down. Each player takes three cards and places them on his stand. To begin the game, one card from the face-down pile is turned over and placed in the middle of the table. When his turn comes, each person plays a card trying to make the maximum possible number of points. If he cannot make any points (that is, if he cannot make an alignment of at least three circles of the same color with his card), he has to play a card anyway. After playing a card, he replaces it with one from the face-down pile.

The players put down one card after another, next to one that is already on the table, until a row of 11 is made. As shown in Figure 8.6a, the cards can be placed either to the right or to the left of the card already placed, but they cannot stick out below or above the alignment.

When one row of 11 cards is completed, the next player can start at A, B, C, or D in Figure 8.6b, and the others proceed in the directions indicated by the arrows. However, once a row is begun, it has to be completed before a new one can be made. (For example, once a player has

Figure 8.6.   *Dominique* or *Domicolor* card configurations.

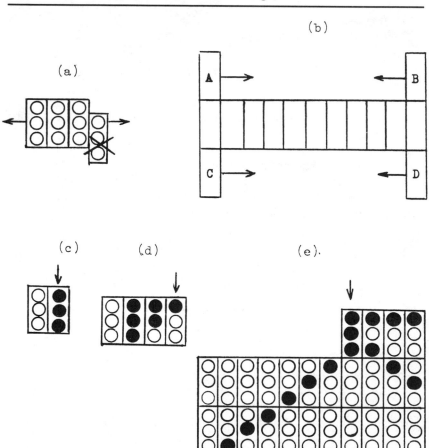

put down a card at A, the next player can put one down either at B or next to A, but not at C or D.) Four rows are made by the end of the game (4 × 11 = 44).

Points: A player wins points by putting a card down in such a way that his cards make a line of three or more circles of the same color, vertically, horizontally, or diagonally. If the circles make a vertical or horizontal line, the player gets 1 point for each circle. If the line is diagonal, he gets 2 points for each circle. Each player announces the number of points he got. If he fails to notice points he could have won, he is not entitled to them after announcing his total. The following are three examples of play and scorekeeping.

In the move shown in Figure 8.6c, the player gets 3 points because he made a vertical line by playing a tile that had three circles all of the same color.

Figure 8.6d shows a move for which the player gets 9 points (3 for the horizontal line and 6 for the diagonal line).

In the move shown in Figure 8.6e, the player gets 29 points (4 for the horizontal line, 3 for the vertical line and 2 × 4 and 2 × 7 respectively for the diagonal lines).

Scores can be kept using the pegboard shown in Figure 8.7. The numerals can be written on the pegboard by hand as shown in this figure. The player has 34 points, and if he gets 8 more points, he will move his tens peg to 40 and his ones peg to 2 (that is, he will add 10 and subtract 2).

Scores can also be kept using paper and pencil. In this case, we ask children to write their total at the end of each turn as shown below. (If they erase the previous total, their arithmetic cannot be checked later by the teacher or anyone else. If they only record the number of points earned on each turn, they will have to add a discouraging number of points at the end of the game and cannot know who is winning from moment to moment.)

Brent	Liz
3	3
+3	+3
6	6
+6	+4
12	10
+3	+6
15	16
+6	+9
21	

Figure 8.7.   A pegboard used for scorekeeping.

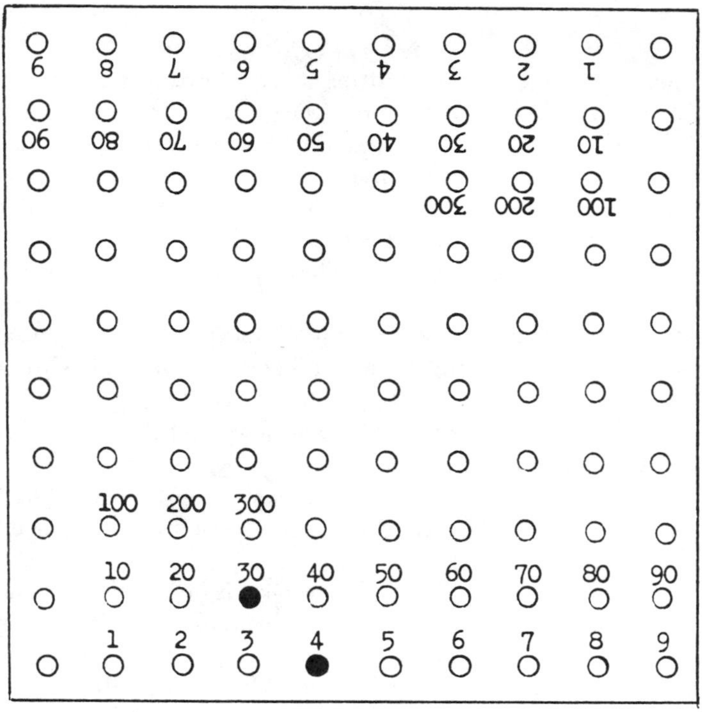

THE SPINNER GAME

Materials: Commercially made wooden bowl (called *Roulette* in the World Wide Games catalog; see Appendix) with numbered holes and a spinner (see Photograph 8.3); six wooden balls; a pegboard or paper and pencil for scorekeeping (see *Dominique* and Figure 8.7).

Play: The printed instructions are good and can be used, but we prefer to modify the rules as follows, to encourage children to make multiples of 10.

The six balls are placed in the middle of the bowl, and the spinner is spun so that it will knock the balls into the numbered holes. Points can be earned only in multiples of 10. For example, if the balls land in the holes numbered 12, 4, 2, 16, 3, and 9, one player may find only 20 points (16 + 4) while another may find 30 points (16 + 12 + 2). A third player, however, may find 40 points (16 + 12 + 9 + 3). The player who gets the greatest number of points is the winner.

While the numbers on the commercially made game work adequately,

Photograph 8.3.   The Spinner Game

the educational value of the game can be improved by taping the following numbers over them: 2, 3, 4, 5, 6, 7, 8, 9, 11, 12, 13, and 24.

TRI-OMINOS

Materials: 56 plastic triangles with a number from 0 to 5 on each corner
of the triangle; paper and pencil for scorekeeping.

This game is commercially made and can be purchased in stores or
ordered by mail (see Appendix).

Play: All the Tri-Ominoes are turned face down and mixed, and each
player takes nine of them if there are two players, or seven of them if
there are three or four players.

One Tri-Omino is placed face up in the middle of the table to begin the
game. The players take turns putting down a Tri-Omino that has a side
bearing the same two numbers as a Tri-Omino that is already on the table,
such as in the move shown in Figure 8.8.

Scores are made by adding the three values shown on the face of the
Tri-Omino that has been played. If the first player begins the game by
playing the topmost Tri-Omino in the figure, she gets 25 points
(5 + 5 + 5, plus a bonus of 10 points for starting the game). The second
player gets 11 points (5 + 5 + 1). The winner is the person who has the

Figure 8.8. The placement of a Tri-Omino.

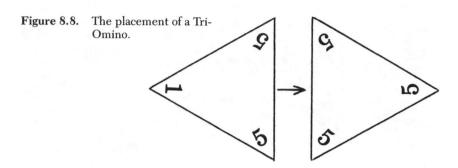

greatest number of points at the end or the first person to reach a certain number of points. Other details of the game—in particular, other bonuses that can be earned—can be found in the instructions that come with the game.

A similar and better game is *Stack-Ominos,* which is found much less frequently in stores. It uses clear plastic tiles, each with up to nine red dots that can be combined in a variety of ways to earn points.

VAGABONDO AND BOOMERANG

Number of Players: Two.

Materials: Plastic pieces such as those shown on the left side of Figure 8.9; gameboard, also shown.

These excellent commercially made games are no longer being produced but are described briefly here in hopes of inspiring someone to produce them.

Play: Each player takes all the 18 pieces of the same color. The value of a piece is the number of squares on its surface. The first player places a piece anywhere except on an X, which indicates that the piece placed on it doubles its value.

All subsequent players must place each piece in such a way that it does not touch any of one's own pieces but touches one of the opponent's pieces at least on one side. A player's score consists of the value of one's own piece played, plus the value of the opponent's piece that it touches. The higher total wins.

BOARD GAMES USING DICE

Board games using dice are singled out as a separate category because dice can be used in a variety of ways for specific purposes, and boards

Figure 8.9. A *Vagabondo* board and pieces.

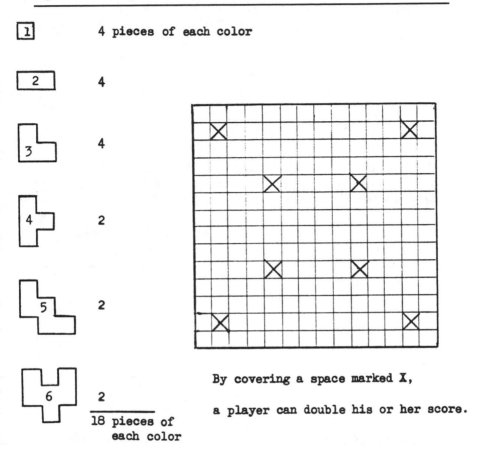

1   4 pieces of each color

2   4

3   4

4   2

5   2

6   2

―――――――
18 pieces of
each color

By covering a space marked X,

a player can double his or her score.

can easily be tailor-made. In this section, we describe the variety of ways in which dice and boards can be used, particularly in games that require players to move from one place to another.

Games Requiring Players to Move Markers from One Place to Another

Various ways of using dice: Dice bearing numerals can, of course, be used instead of regular dice with dots. Ten-sided dice and 12-sided dice permit the increase of addends to 12. In Double *Parcheesi* (Kamii, 1985, pp. 148–149) players move twice as many spaces as the number rolled. For example, if a player rolls a 5, he moves 10 spaces. Dice can also be used for various other purposes such as the following eight:

1. *Set partitioning of 10.* Players subtract the amount of their roll from 10, to determine how many spaces they may advance. Thus, if a player rolls a 1, she can advance 9 spaces; if she rolls a 2, she can advance 8 spaces; and so forth.

2. *Set partitioning of 7.* Players can advance by the number that is on the bottom of the die, but no one can look on the bottom. If a player rolls a 6, for example, he can move 1 space.

3. *Determining odd and even numbers.* A player can advance only if the total of the two dice is even; if it is odd, the person cannot move.

4. *Subtraction.* The smaller of the two numbers rolled must be subtracted from the larger.

5. *Addition and subtraction.* The numbers on two dice of the same color must be added, and the number on the die of a different color must be subtracted. If the result is smaller than zero, the player must move backward.

6. *Learning doubles and doubles + 1.* Doubles are spontaneously used by many children, who change 3 + 4 to (3 + 3) + 1, for example. Teachers can experiment with putting different numerals on two six-sided dice. To encourage the use of doubles, try putting only two numbers on each die (e.g., each die has 3 threes and 3 fours on it). Following are several possibilities:

Numbers on each die	*Possible combinations*
3 and 4	3 + 3, 3 + 4, and 4 + 4
4 and 5	4 + 4, 4 + 5, and 5 + 5
5 and 6	5 + 5, 5 + 6, and 6 + 6
6 and 7	6 + 6, 6 + 7, and 7 + 7
7 and 8	7 + 7, 7 + 8, and 8 + 8

   Another variation is putting only three numbers on each of two dice (e.g., each die has 2 threes, 2 fours, and 2 fives on it). Then there are the following possible combinations:

Numbers on each die	*Possible combinations*
3, 4, and 5	3 + 3, 3 + 4, 3 + 5, 4 + 4, 4 + 5, 5 + 5
4, 5, and 6	4 + 4, 4 + 5, 4 + 6, 5 + 5, 5 + 6, 6 + 6
5, 6, and 7	5 + 5, 5 + 6, 5 + 7, 6 + 6, 6 + 7, 7 + 7

   When addends have a difference of two, as in 3 + 5, children sometimes change them to doubles (4 + 4 in the case of 3 + 5).

7. *Using combinations that make 10.* If one die has nines on all sides and the other one is a regular die, it occurs to some children to change 9 + 5 to (9 + 1) + 4, for example. The first die can also be made to have eights on all sides, or sevens, or sixes.

8. *Making multiples of 10.* Six (or more) dice can be used for a game that requires the creation of multiples of 10. For example, if the numbers 1, 2, 3, 4, 5, and 6 turn up on six dice, one player may find only 10 points (5 + 3 + 2), while another player may find 20 points (6 + 5 + 4 + 3 + 2). The players can advance one space for every 10 made, or earn a bottlecap or a dime in play money for every 10.

Various ways of making boards: Boards can vary in shape and content, and some commercially made games use only one marker while others use four. It is, of course, possible to use two or three markers.

By "content" we mean the theme used in a game such as dinosaurs, space shuttles, and football. Although some commercially made games such as *Parcheesi* and *Sorry* do not involve any contents, we have found that a theme can contribute greatly to the popularity of a game.

Parcheesi and *Sorry* involve a path that goes around the edges of the board. Other shapes are a winding path, an 8-shaped path, a spiral path, a circular path, and a zigzag path. Hideout and Parachutes respectively illustrate a circular and a zigzag path.

HIDEOUT

Materials: A board such as the one shown in Figure 8.10 and Photograph 8.4. (Arranging self-adhesive labels and drawing circles on a checkerboard is one way of making this board. Checkerboards are inexpensive, sturdy, and easy to store.) Two dice; a marker for each player.

Play: Each player puts her marker on one of the starting spaces. Players take turns rolling the dice and moving as many spaces clockwise as indicated. When a player lands on a space with an arrow, she follows the arrow into the space indicated. On her next turn, she moves clockwise as many spaces as indicated by the dice.

If a player's move brings her to a space already occupied, she must move her marker to where it was before. If a player lands on a green space, she gets an extra turn. If she lands on a red space, she will miss her next turn. The winner is the first to reach the hideout in the center.

PARACHUTES

Number of Players: Two or three.

Materials: The board shown in Figure 8.11; two dice; a marker for each player.

Lee Isaac

Photograph 8.4. Hideout

Play: The object of the game is to be the first one to reach the treasure. Each player chooses his parachute (A, B, or C) and puts his marker on it. Players take turns rolling the dice. To get out of the parachute, each player has to get one of three totals: Player A—4, 6, or 11; Player B—10, 8, or 3; and Player C—4, 8, or 3. Once on a number, a player can move one space at a time, to a space next to the one he is on—horizontally, vertically, or diagonally—by getting a total shown on one of those spaces. For example, if Player A gets out on 6, he can move to 4, 9, 7, 6, or 11. The game ends when one of the players exits the columns of numbers, thus reaching the treasure.

Other Ideas for Using Dice and/or Boards

The teacher can write "× 2" and "× 3" on various spaces of an otherwise unmarked path. If a player lands on a space marked "× 2," he doubles the number rolled the next time and advances his marker by that number. If he lands on a space marked "× 3," he triples the next roll and moves accordingly.

For low-level children, the teacher can make a game such as Doubles Cover-Up, which is shown in Figure 8.12. Doubles Cover-Up also requires a die and as many poker chips as there are numbers to cover. Two players sit on opposite sides of the board. If a player rolls 1, she covers

Figure 8.10. A Hideout board.

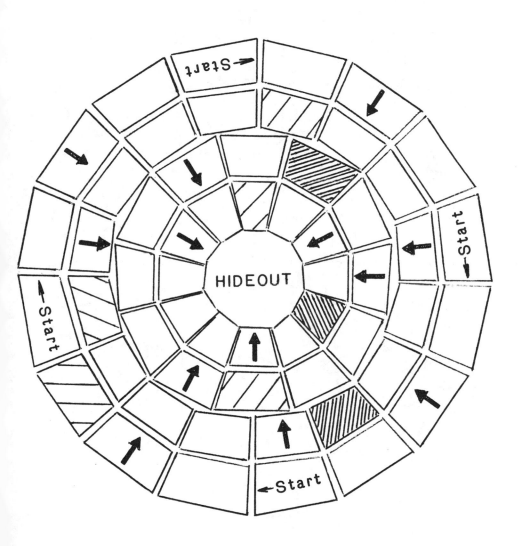

Figure 8.11. A Parachutes board (invented by Nicole Bordier).

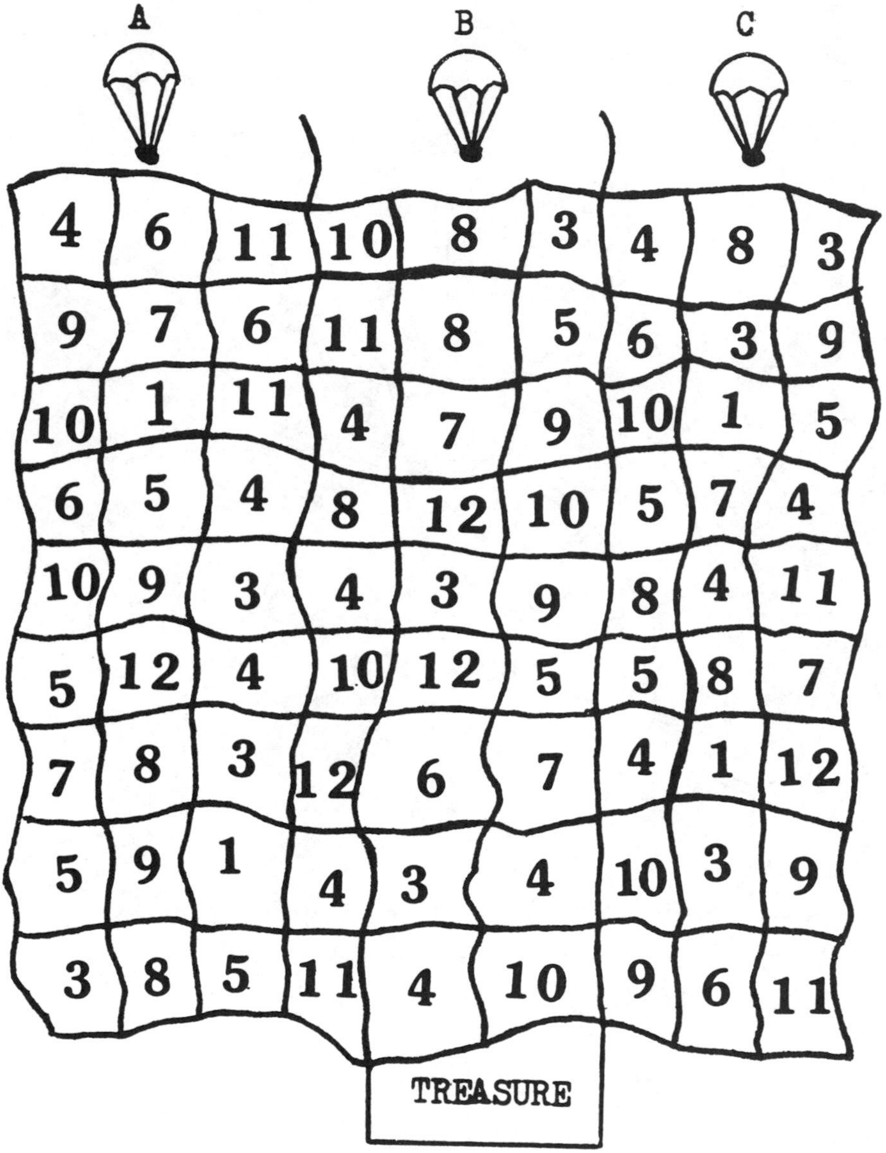

Figure 8.12. A Doubles
Cover-Up board.

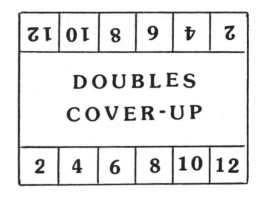

the 2 on her side of the board; and if she rolls 2, she covers 4, and so
forth. If a number is already covered, the player cannot cover anything.
The person who covers all six numbers first is the winner.

The preceding game can be modified into Doubles + 1 Cover-Up. In
this case, a 10-sided die can be used with 20 poker chips, and the board
would include doubles + 1 from 3 to 21. If a player rolls a 1, she covers
3 (1 + 1 + 1); and if she rolls a 2, she covers 5 (2 + 2 + 1), and so
forth.

GAMES INVOLVING PHYSICAL-KNOWLEDGE ACTIVITIES

Examples of games involving physical-knowledge activities (Kamii &
DeVries, 1978) are those that require aiming, such as basketball, pool,
and golf. These games all involve an object's reaction to the subject's action of throwing, hitting, kicking, and so forth. They are treated as a
separate category because some of them can be used outdoors, and the
addends can be anything ranging from 0 to 3,000.

The advantage of this category of games is that some children learn
much better when they can move around. For example, Linda Joseph
taped a 3 × 3 grid on a desk, put a number in each section of the grid,
and let children take turns throwing three cotton balls (or beanbags) onto
the desk. A player's score on each turn was the total indicated by the 3
cotton balls. The players calculated a new total at the end of each turn.
For some children, the freedom to move made an enormous difference
in their enjoyment and learning of addition.

The following are some examples of physical-knowledge activities,
grouped according to children's actions, such as throwing and hitting.
Some are homemade games, while others are commercially made. Many

commercially made games can be adapted and made inexpensively at home.

Throwing

TOSS GAME

Materials: A floor or desktop target; three poker chips. Target can be made from spongy foam packing material with round holes cut in it. Numbers are printed beside each hole, with the bull's-eye having the highest value and the numbers getting smaller as they move away from the center.

This is a variation on the game using a grid and cotton balls or beanbags, just described.

Play: In this case, each turn consists of tossing three poker chips onto the target.

BASKETBALL

Materials: Old tire and rope; balls or beanbag. Old tires can be suspended and used for a "basket."

Play: Children throw basketball through the tire, getting 2 points per basket. Repeated addition of the two points earned for each "basket" leads to multiplication.

RING TOSS

Materials: A wooden plaque with hooks and numbers on it, as shown in Photograph 8.5; 5 rubber rings; paper and pencil for scorekeeping. The game is available through World Wide Games (see Appendix) or it can easily be made at home.

Play: This is an old British pub game. It comes with 13 rings, but we prefer to use only 5 of them. After throwing the 5 rings, the children add the total to their previous score. The children decide where they must stand to aim, and when the game ends.

SAFE DART GAME

Materials: Dartboard and 3 safety darts, as shown in Photograph 8.6; paper and pencil for scorekeeping. The game is available through The Paragon (see Appendix).

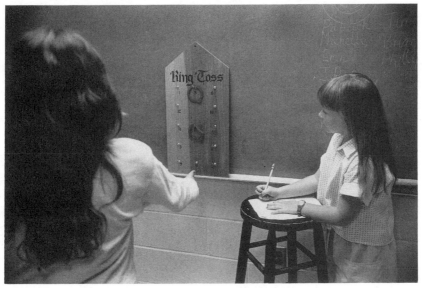

Wayne Hamby

Photograph 8.5.   *Ring Toss*

Play: The possible numbers of points are 100, 75, 50, and 25, which are just right for second graders. The players decide where they must stand to aim, and how many turns each person will have.

Hitting with a Stick

GOLF, HOCKEY, AND POOL

Materials: These are all similar games that can be set up with an enclosure made with blocks. A stick, a chopstick, or a long block can be used to hit a ball or disk. The target can be a ball, an area taped on the floor, or an opening between two blocks. Children can decide on the number of points each successful attempt will earn.

Dropping

REGIE OR *PASSE MURAILLE*

Materials: This commercially made game (*Regie* in German or *Passe Muraille* in French) does not seem to be available in the United States. We hope that our mentioning it might encourage someone to import it or manufacture a similar but sturdier game.

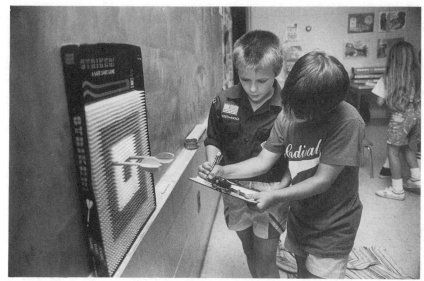

Wayne Hamby

Photograph 8.6.   *Safety Darts*

Play: As can be seen in Photograph 8.7, the object of the game is to slide parts of a "wall" to make a chip fall into a section of the box underneath that earns the most points. The points on this particular model are too easy and require modification.

Other Physical Actions

TIDDLY WINKS

Materials: The commercially made game comes with a dish divided into sections numbered 5, 10, 25, and 100. A paper plate can be used in a similar way with plastic chips.

Play: By pressing on the edge of a plastic chip with the edge of another chip, players try to make the first chip jump into the dish. They add the number of points the section of the dish earns. Children decide how far away from the dish they must place the chip they aim, and how many times they may try on each turn.

LEVERS

Materials: Base-10 blocks make a good lever, as can be seen in Figure 8.13.

Photograph 8.7.   *Regie* or *Passe Muraille*

Play: Levers can be used in a way similar to *Tiddly Winks*. Children can set up small, shallow boxes and make up a point system.

SHOOT THE MOON

Materials: This is a commercially made game (see Appendix).

Play: This is an excellent game of physics in which the child has to make a steel ball go up an incline by manipulating the distance between two steel rods (see Photograph 8.8). A player tries to get the ball as far up the incline as possible before it loses momentum or slips between the rods.

Figure 8.13.   A lever made with base-10 blocks.

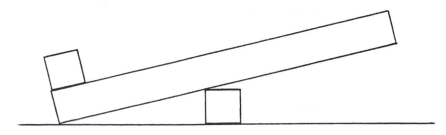

Wayne Hamby

Photograph 8.8. *Shoot the Moon*

The farther the ball goes before it drops into one of the holes below, the more points the player makes. The point system for *Shoot the Moon* and two possible modifications can be seen in the following list:

Shoot the Moon	*Modification 1*	*Modification 2*
− 250	− 10	− 11
250	10	11
500	20	22
1000	30	33
2000	50	55
3000	100	100

THE SPINNER GAME

The Spinner Game, described on page 120, should also be mentioned here to complete the classification of games involving physical-knowledge activities.

GAMES INVOLVING MONEY

Games involving money are singled out as a separate category because money is especially important in real life and its units foster thinking about fives, tens, and hundreds. These games involve addends of 1, 5, 10, 25, 50, 100, and 500.

THE ALLOWANCE GAME

Materials: Commercially made game (see Appendix), which comes with a board, play money (20 5-dollar bills, 25 1-dollar bills, 20 quarters, 20 dimes, and 20 nickels), a die, 4 markers, and 8 chips.

Play: The children move a marker the number of spaces indicated by the die. They then follow the directions on the space they land for earning or spending money. For example, one space says, "Deliver papers. Earn 85¢," and another says, "Buy school stuff. Spend $1.00." The first person to have a total of $10.00 is the winner.

COIN DICE

Materials: Three coin dice (available from Didax Educational Resources and Educational Teaching Aids, see Appendix) showing the following coins: a penny (on two of the six sides), a nickel, a dime, a quarter, and a half-dollar. Also, the following 68 cards (two of each unless indicated otherwise in parentheses; the cents should sometimes be written with a cents sign and sometimes with a decimal point):

3¢	35¢	75¢ (1)
7¢	36¢	76¢ (3)
11¢	40¢	80¢
12¢	45¢	85¢
15¢ (1)	51¢	$1.00
16¢	52¢ (3)	$1.01
20¢	55¢	$1.05
21¢	56¢ (3)	$1.10
25¢	60¢	$1.25
27¢	61¢ (3)	$1.50 (1)
30¢ (1)	65¢	
31¢	70¢	

Play: Each player takes 16 cards and makes a 4 × 4 arrangement, as for a Bingo game (see Figure 8.14). The players take turns rolling the three dice. Everybody who has a card corresponding to the total of the three dice turns it over. The person who turns over four cards in a row vertically, horizontally, or diagonally first is the winner.

As a variation, the first person who first turns over two rows of four

Figure 8.14.   The arrangement of
16 cards in Coin
Dice.

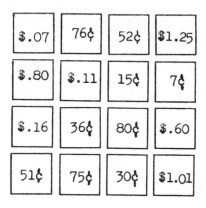

cards can be the winner. Another variation is turning over the four corner
cards first.

Games Involving Premultiplication

Multiplication is usually introduced in third grade. Therefore, the games
mentioned in this section are for the more advanced second graders and
refer to repeated addition as a prelude to multiplication.

Since there is an overlap between this "premultiplication" and addition, certain games categorized under addition also belong to the present
group. An example is the dice game using a board on which certain spaces
were marked "× 2" and "× 3." Another example is the games involving
physical-knowledge activities in which players can score points for each
success. If a basket is worth 7 points, for example, 3 baskets would earn
21 points.

Two other games are described below. One is a card game called I
Doubt It, and the other, a dice game called Choose.

I DOUBT IT

Number of Players: Three or four.

Materials: A deck of 40 homemade cards, four each of 10 numbers such
as the following combinations:

    2, 4, 6, 8, 10, 12, 14, 16, 18, and 20
    5, 10, 15, 20, 25, 30, 35, 40, 45, and 50
    1, 3, 5, 7, 9, 11, 13, 15, 17, and 19

Play: All 40 cards are dealt. The first player puts a 2 in the middle of the table, face down, saying, "Two." The next player then puts a 4 on top of the 2, also face down, saying, "Four." The third player continues with a 6, saying, "Six." Any player who does not have the card she needs substitutes another card, hoping to get away with this bluff.

Anyone who thinks that a card other than the one announced has been played says, "I doubt it." If the doubt is verified, the person caught must take all the cards on the table and add them to her hand. If the doubt is not verified, the accuser has to take all the cards. Play continues until a person wins by getting rid of all her cards.

As a variation, this game can be played using the numbers in descending order (20, 18, 16, etc.).

CHOOSE

Materials: Six cubes or blank dice, each with six different numbers and five different colors on its sides; paper and pencil for scorekeeping. Self-adhesive labels (such as Dennison No. 43-851) in assorted colors can be placed on the dice, and numbers can be written on them with the combinations listed below. (Scotch tape protects the dice from wear.)

The six colors (column headings) indicate the six sides of each die. The numbers are those that must be written on each color. For example, on the first die, 1 should be written on the green label, 2 on the blue label, 3 and 4 on orange labels, 5 on the red label, and 6 on the yellow one.

	Green	Red	Blue	Yellow	Orange	Orange
First die	1	5	2	6	3	4
Second die	2	1	6	5	3	4
Third die	3	6	4	1	2	5
Fourth die	4	2	5	3	1	6
Fifth die	5	4	3	2	1	6
Sixth die	6	3	1	4	2	5

Play: The object of the game is to get the greatest number of points with dice of the same color or of the same number. In each turn, a player can roll the dice three times.

After the first throw, the player decides if he will choose the same color or the same number. He sets aside those he wants to use and rolls the other dice again. He can roll all six dice again if the outcome of the first throw was not favorable.

After the second roll, the player sets aside the dice he wants to use and throws the others. He may also change his objective, depending on what he has gotten so far. If nothing encouraging has come out so far, he may roll all six dice again.

After the third throw, the points obtained are written on the scoring sheet and added to the previous total. If, for example, the player gets 3 fours, his score is 12. If, on the other hand, he gets 3 green sides with a 6, a 5, and a 3 on them, his score is 14.

When all six dice show the same color or the same number, this is called "Double Choose" and the number of points is doubled. For example, if the player gets 6 sixes, his score is 72 ($6 \times 6 \times 2$ or $(6 + 6 + 6 + 6 + 6 + 6) + 36$).

Games Involving Subtraction

CARD GAMES

SALUTE!

Number of Players: Three.

Materials: A deck of playing cards.

Play: The face cards are removed, leaving 40 cards in all. Ace represents 1. The cards are dealt to two of the three players. The two players sit facing each other, and each holds his stack face down. Simultaneously, the two take the top cards of their respective piles and say, "Salute!" as they hold them next to their faces in such a way that they can see only the other person's card.

The third player announces the total of the two cards. Each of the other two players guesses the number on his card, by subtracting the opponent's number from the total. The person who shouts the correct number first takes both cards. The winner is the person who collects the most cards.

As a variation, this game can be played with multiplication and division, too.

THE ZERO GAME

Materials: A deck of playing cards; bottlecaps or pencil and paper for scorekeeping.

Play: All the odd-numbered hearts are eliminated from the deck. The

Lee Isaac

Photograph 8.9.   Card game

face cards can be either eliminated or count as 10s. Each player receives three cards, which she may hold and look at. The players take turns putting down a card face up, and subtracting the number on it from the previous total. The game starts with 30, and if the first player puts down a 10, she says "Twenty" as she puts it down. If the next player puts down a 5, she says, "Fifteen." The person who goes below 0 is the loser of the round and receives a tally mark or bottlecap. The game is over when someone gets 10 tally marks.

The hearts (even-numbered) are "plus" cards, so the numbers on them are added to the previous total.

Each time a player puts down a card, she replaces it with one from the drawing pile so that she will have three cards again.

ADDITION AND SUBTRACTION SHAPES

Materials: Two sets of 24 sturdy plastic triangles each (similar to those used for *Tens and Twenties*.) One set has purple lines and involves addition. The other has yellow lines and involves subtraction. The two sets can be combined but can also be used separately. This game is commercially made (see Appendix).

Play: Although this is not a card game, strictly speaking, it is played like one. The triangles are placed face down on the table, and the players each take an equal number, such as four. One triangle is turned over in the middle of the table to start the game. In the subtraction version of the game, the players take turns matching a problem side (such as 13 − 4) to an answer side (such as 9) or an answer side to a problem side.

Each time a player puts down a triangle, she replaces it with one from the face-down pile. A player unable to make a match must continue to take triangles until she gets one that she can play.

The winner is the first person to use up all her pieces.

BOARD GAMES

THREE-IN-A-ROW

Number of Players: Two.

Materials: A board such as the one shown in Figure 8.15; 2 small rings; 16 tiles or buttons, 8 each of two colors.

Play: This game is similar to Four-in-a-Row (see page 113). Each player takes all the tiles of one color. Each in turn chooses a number from square A and a number from square B and puts a ring on each number. He then subtracts the smaller from the larger and finds the answer in the large square and covers it with a tile. If the number is already covered, this turn is wasted. The first player to get three tiles in a row—vertically, horizontally, or diagonally—is the winner.

ZIGZAZ

Materials: The Zigzag board shown in Figure 8.16; three dice; a marker for each player.

Play: All the markers are placed on "Start." The object of the game is to reach the goal first.

The players take turns rolling the three dice. The three numbers rolled can be added or subtracted in any order of one's choice. For example, if a 2, a 3, and a 4 come up, they can make the following:

$$9 \ (2 + 3 + 4)$$
$$1 \ (2 + 3 - 4 \ \text{or} \ 3 + 2 - 4)$$
$$3 \ (2 + 4 - 3 \ \text{or} \ 4 + 2 - 3 \ \text{or} \ 4 - 3 + 2 \ \text{or} \ 2 - 3 + 4)$$
$$5 \ (4 - 2 + 3 \ \text{or} \ 4 + 3 - 2 \ \text{or} \ 3 - 2 + 4 \ \text{or} \ 3 + 4 - 2)$$

The player can thus put her marker on 9, 1, 3, or 5.

Figure 8.15. Three-in-a-Row.

14	13
12	11

A

9	7
5	3

B

6	10	7	9
2	4	5	3
7	5	6	8
4	9	8	11

Figure 8.16. A Zigzag board.

Goal								
2	9	7	4	6	8	7	5	9
5	4	3	8	9	1	2	5	4
8	7	6	3	5	4	9	2	7
6	2	5	7	8	7	6	4	3
8	7	3	6	4	1	2	5	1
2	4	8	5	9	7	6	8	5
7	3	2	1	5	4	5	7	3
5	8	7	2	8	7	6	9	8
8	4	5	6	7	3	6	5	3
2	8	1	8	10	7	9	4	5
7	5	6	9	4	2	8	1	3
Start								

Thereafter, a player can move only one space at a time, forward, backward, sideways, or diagonally. For example, if a player is on 5 in the bottom row, she can move to 7, 2, 8, 1, or 6.

Other Games

There are a few games that do not neatly fit the preceding classification. One is called The Hundred Board, which involves the written decimal system rather than any specific operation. The second category consists of games invented by children, and the third one is games for the whole class.

THE HUNDRED BOARD

Number of Players: Two or three.

Materials: One hundred tiles bearing the numbers 1 through 100; a board with a 10 × 10 grid, on which the tiles can be placed. (The board and tiles are listed in the catalogs of Creative Publications and Cuisenaire Co. of America; see Appendix).

Play: This game is good for children to think about 1 more, 1 less, 10 more, 10 less, 10 more + 1, 10 more − 1, 10 less + 1, 10 less − 1, and their spatial arrangement. The Hundred Board has numbers on one side and only a grid on the other side. The side with only the grid is used in this game. All the tiles are turned down so that no one can see the numbers on them. Each player then takes eight tiles and keeps them face up in front of himself.

One tile is then turned up and placed in the appropriate space on the board. (It is surprising how hard it is for many second graders to decide where 43 should go, for example.) The players then take turns placing one tile on the board at a time and replacing it with one from the face-down pile.

Only tiles that touch either a side or a corner of a tile already on the board can be played. For example, if 68 has been placed on the board, the tiles that can be played next are 57, 58, 59, 67, 69, 77, 78, and 79, as shown in Figure 8.17. (This may seem easy, but a surprising number of second graders do not notice that they can play the 57, for example.)

If a player does not have a tile that can be played, he has to miss a turn and take one from those that are face down. The first person to use up all

Figure 8.17. The placement of
numbers on the Hun-
dred Board.

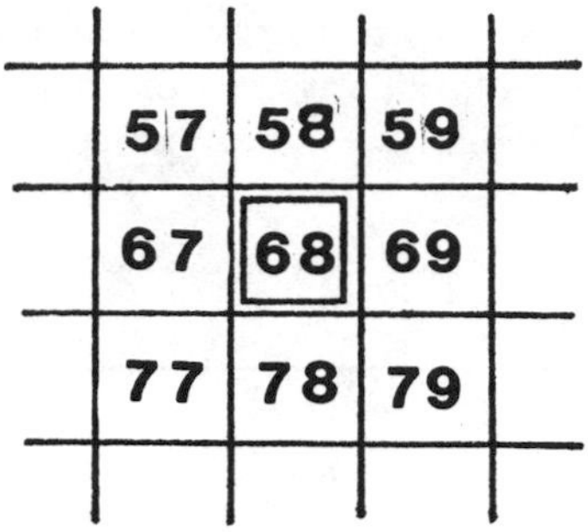

his tiles is the winner.

A variation is to start the game with 1 in the space where 5 usually goes.

GAMES INVENTED BY CHILDREN

Children become ingenious about inventing games, and this invention is good for the development of their ability to think creatively and to exchange viewpoints with others. One day, for example, Linda Joseph came with a wooden ball about 2 inches in diameter and asked the class if they could think of a game that used it. One child immediately suggested rolling the ball to knock down wooden dominoes. A player's score would be the number of points on all the dominoes knocked down, the child said.

Games invented by children are particularly good because children are invested in the games they and/or their classmates invent. Below is an example of such a game. It seems frustrating toward the end, but children have an enormous amount of respect for the rules that *they* make.

ONE HUNDRED FIFTY, EXACTLY

Number of Players: Two.

Materials: The numbered side of the Hundred Board described in the game by this name (with numbers 1 through 100 in a 10 × 10 grid arrangement, where the top row is 1 through 10, the next is 11 through 20, and so on); three dice; a marker for each player.

Play: The players take turns rolling the three dice and adding the results. If the first player gets a total of 16, for example, he places his marker on 16. If he gets a total of 12 on his next turn, he mentally adds this number to his previous total and moves his marker to 28, and so forth.

The object of the game is to reach 100 and then start at the top at 1 again and go to 50 (which makes 150). If a player does not land exactly on 50, he subtracts his roll and goes backward. He continues to go back and forth on subsequent turns until he lands exactly on 50.

GAMES FOR THE ENTIRE CLASS

All the games described in this chapter so far are those for small groups of two to four children. It is sometimes desirable to play games with the entire class to enhance a feeling of community in the room. Tic-Tac-15 was described earlier in this chapter as a team game that the class plays often, with great excitement. Around the World, which was mentioned in Chapter 6, is also an exciting game children beg to play.

What's My Rule? is not exactly a game in which children try to win, but it is a whole-class, game-like activity. Because it has a rule stating that no one can state the rule, it cleverly involves all the class members who are at different levels of development.

For example, the teacher writes 3 on the chalkboard, draws an arrow from it, and then writes 7 (see Figure 8.18a). She then writes another number and an arrow as shown in the same figure.

Figure 8.18.   An example of What's My Rule?

(a)	3 → 7	(c)	3 → 7
	7 →		7 → 11
			18 → 22
			25 → 29
(b)	3 → 7		36 → 40
	7 → 11		48 → 52
	18 →		59 →

The children who have an idea about the number that might go after the arrow raise their hands. If the child called on says, "11," the teacher writes it and goes on to write another number and an arrow as shown in Figure 8.18b. The rule of this game is that the children can give numbers generated by following the rule they hypothesize, but they cannot state the rule itself.

The beauty of this game is that the less advanced children can have time to think, without having the question answered by the more advanced pupils. In fact, the less advanced children can use the numbers given by the more advanced ones. By the time the column looks like Figure 8.18c, all the children raise their hands.

The game ends when someone gives an incorrect number or says, "Disagree." The teacher then asks, "What's my rule?" and calls on someone to give it. She then starts a new series.

This game can, of course, be adapted for all the other operations.

CONCLUSION

We would like to conclude with a few remarks about scorekeeping, which is required in many of the games described in this chapter. We recommend scorekeeping either with paper and pencil or with the pegboard described with *Dominique* or *Domicolor* (p. 117). The pegboard has many advantages such as inspiring children to think about adding 8, for example, by adding 10 and subtracting 2. However, this kind of thinking is too advanced for many second graders.

Paper and pencil is practical for all second graders, but children tend to do two things that should be discouraged: (1) writing numbers in a column throughout the game instead of adding each score to the previous total at the end of each turn and (2) erasing the previous total and writing only the last total at the end of each turn.

The first tendency is undesirable because players cannot tell who is winning from one moment to the next, and because children do not learn much arithmetic this way. The neck-and-neck competition is part of the motivational benefit of games that should be used.

There is, incidentally, a world of difference between this kind of competition in a game and the kind of competition that schools often use to get children to study for the highest grade in the class, the next highest grade, and so on. In games, children set the rules, they choose to play or not to play, and there is no official recognition of the winner after the game is over. In traditional schools, on the other hand, adults make all the rules, and children do not have any choice about competing or not competing with their classmates.

Children's tendency to erase is undesirable because they waste time that could be spent thinking, and because the teacher cannot see the children's work afterwards. By examining children's score sheets afterwards, the teacher can tell which game each child played, what numbers he or she worked with, and what errors were made, if any. These score sheets serve as records of children's progress throughout the year, and enable the teacher to steer individual children toward certain games that are at their levels.

Children respond well to the teacher when they are given the above reasons for having to keep score in a certain way. These reasons are very different from traditional instruction, which requires them to write the "right" symbols in the "right" way. Writing to know who is winning in a game is very different from writing on a worksheet only to obey the teacher. Writing in a way that the teacher will understand is likewise very different from writing in the "correct" form just because it is the conventional mathematical form.

Autonomy is both moral and intellectual, and this goal guides the teacher in deciding how to interact with children during each moment of the math hour. When we interact with children in ways that correspond to *their* needs and thoughts, we help them develop morally and intellectually from within. When we interact with them in ways that impose our adult standards, on the other hand, we help them learn only to cope with us from one moment to the next.

Part IV

A TEACHER'S PERSPECTIVE AND EVALUATION

CHAPTER 9

Metamorphosis

by Linda Joseph

I had taught second grade for 10 years and always thought I was a "good" teacher, who supplemented the basic mathematics textbook with manipulatives to illustrate my points. When Connie Kamii came into my room, therefore, I thought she would be impressed with my class's performance. Instead, she said, "Your children are not thinking." I realized she was right, because I had often said to myself, "Some of them are not using their heads." Her idea was to use situations in daily living and games to encourage children to build their own knowledge of arithmetic.

I was afraid of launching into unfamiliar territory and of giving up my beloved teacher's manual; however, I decided to see for myself if there could be a better way of teaching arithmetic. I began to change my strategy. I started planning ways of challenging the children instead of providing them with model solutions to imitate. I was skeptical, but, as my principal said, the old ways didn't work, either.

Most of the first year was a replication of *Young Children Reinvent Arithmetic* (Kamii, 1985), so I will briefly describe my observations of the first year and go on to the second, third, and fourth years.

THE FIRST YEAR

Throughout each school day, I encouraged the children to make decisions concerning numbers, whenever possible. For example, I encouraged them to divide birthday treats and to tell me what to write in the daily attendance report and lunch orders for the cafeteria. I even began to say, "We have wasted 5 minutes so far. If we combine 5 minutes for everybody here, how many minutes have we wasted all together?" Math was thus no longer something dished out on a piece of paper that was to be filled in with right or wrong answers. In fact, paper was rarely used at all. Math became something that occurred whenever a question concerning numbers came up, and I stopped saying, "We aren't doing that today" or, "Wait until math time."

I found that autonomy was necessary for games to succeed. If children came over asking me to settle arguments during game time, I told them that they could handle them themselves. I knew the children were getting the idea when I overheard someone say one day, "She won't do anything right now. Let's go back and play." At the end of games, however, I sometimes asked, "Were there any problems today?" or, "Did anyone do something that you would like to tell the class about?" This was the time when agitated children could ask for suggestions about their earlier complaints. The other pupils offered ideas about how to handle problems, such as voting to send a misbehaving child back to his or her seat. These discussions led to the children becoming more self-governing and left time for me to concentrate on the games. I had not counted on this bonus.

I found that, as my role changed from being the omniscient authority to one who asked for suggestions, I had to shift my focus away from myself as the central figure around whom classroom life revolved. This was not limited to math time. Instead of giving directions, I asked for children's ideas, such as where to put their art work while it dried. This process, which Piaget calls "de-centering," challenged me to think about each situation from the child's point of view. It was the hardest thing for me to do.

Nobody had ever told me to make math fun. Nobody said, "Get excited." But that is what happened when I allowed, encouraged, and even enticed children to construct numerical ideas for themselves. I, too, invented my own procedures for encouraging children to construct.

I had begun the year with a lot of uncertainty; however, having seen how positively the children reacted, I could hardly wait to start the second year. I was curious to see if the next class could attain the same heights.

THE SECOND YEAR

Starting the second year was easier, since I had survived one year without math workbooks. In addition, the group of children coming to me for second grade had already spent first grade in a classroom where Connie Kamii's approach was used.

Since this year most of the children were familiar with games from first grade, I selected some that they already knew and put them out on a shelf. I then briefly reviewed a few games at a time and asked the children to choose a partner and a game. I gave guidance to those who needed it, and the first few days were devoted only to games.

While the children were playing games, I tested them individually on sums up to 9 + 9, to determine who knew their sums quickly and who counted on fingers (see Kamii, 1985, Tables 5.1 and 5.2). (I did this twice more during the year, while the children played games.) With this knowledge, I gently steered children toward games that would help in their weak areas. For example, to those weak in doubles, I suggested that they might like to play Double *Parcheesi* (Kamii, 1985, p. 148–149).

I liked to know and remember who was playing which games, so I began to keep a small notebook in which I jotted down names and games and any difficulties the students were encountering. The best way for me to tell a child's ability, though, was actually to play with him or her. By playing with the children, I could assess firsthand how well they reasoned with numbers.

When parents came for conferences, I could give specific facts, such as, "Your child knows the sums up to 10 quickly and easily, as well as the doubles up to 7 + 7. He has difficulty with sums between 11 and 18; so we have been playing Quince together." If a parent offered to help by drilling the child with flashcards, I quickly declined. I showed the article by Madell (1985) saying that memorization of "facts" is not desirable, and I asked them to help instead by playing games in which the child does most of the decision making.

Also in September, I began the discussions described in Chapter 6. This was an area lacking during the first year. These discussions were important for the exchange of ideas, and they proved to be most beneficial. My purpose was not just to get the class to agree on an answer; it was also to help children feel comfortable enough to present their ideas, even if they sometimes got stuck without getting the final answer. I also wanted them to see that there were many "right" ways to solve a problem. The discussions in September usually followed half an hour of playing games. By October, however, I had reversed the order and was beginning the math period with the discussions.

By early October, the children were accustomed to voicing their opinions by saying "Agree!" or "Disagree!" and had become adept at noticing at what point a classmate's thinking became flawed. It was not unusual, for example, to hear one pupil say to another, "I agree with the first part, but you forgot to add the other 10; so I disagree." The children had to choose their words carefully to make their ideas clear enough for the others to understand. If not, someone was bound to say, "That doesn't make sense." My role as teacher, then, was one of helping the children clarify their statements. They came to expect a variety of answers, since I often listed them on the board. Some children remarked, "Wait. I want to check mine," before explanations were begun, especially if there were many different answers.

Occasionally, I asked the children to write their answers on paper. This helped me know who wrote 10013 for 113, for example. When this happened, I asked the class how they thought the number should be written. Discussions of this type seemed to result in permanent learning much more often than did direct teaching.

By November, the range of ability had begun to widen tremendously. Having become adept at double-column addition, some children began requesting "something harder." The discussions then began to focus on whatever these challenge seekers wanted to do. If they said, "Give us something in the hundreds," a few children attempted those. By continuing to give a variety of easier problems, I could keep the others involved, too.

At that time of year, interest in games was lower because of the rapid development in problem-solving ability. The children often said, "Let's do brain exercises." That was our favorite term for problem solving at the board. I was thrilled with their excitement about this type of problem. They were stretching their ability and loving it. They especially enjoyed story problems involving multiplication, which they tackled in original ways. To do 12×6, for example, they made the following computations: $12 + 12 = 24$, $24 + 24 = 48$, $48 + 24 = 72$. No problem was too hard for them, as long as I gave them enough time to work it out. As a teacher, I was more like a scribe, writing on the board for the children while they concentrated on the thinking portion, or asking just the right questions if they were floundering. When children get their own answer, one that makes sense to them, they are jubilant and gain confidence.

During a faculty meeting in January, a first-grade teacher asked Connie Kamii if we as teachers should be providing specific activities with subtraction. Her reply was that there was no point in "teaching" subtraction in first grade (see Kamii, 1985, Chapter 6) and that children would be able to subtract when they were sufficiently adept at adding. Feeling that my children were adding quite well, I challenged them with the following problem:

$$\begin{array}{r} 46 \\ -18 \\ \hline \end{array}$$

One child best summed up the class's feelings by saying, "That's the hard kind." After a long pause, Eric said, "Forty take away 10 is 30, and 8 take away 6 is 2." Being familiar with this kind of error, I shook my head and told the child that he could not subtract upside down. He ignored me and continued, "And 30 take away 2 is 28." I was dumbfounded to find that he got the correct answer, so I wrote a similar problem on the board. His method worked again and again. Eric explained that you could take only 6 from 6, but you still had to take 2 more from somewhere; so you took it from 30. My reaction was one of wonderment. It was such a simple solution. Other equally impressive methods followed on subsequent days.

I was becoming convinced by now that games and discussions were much better than drill sheets. The children reacted positively to my excitement and were willing to try any kind of problem. They even tackled division problems with ease. Their method of dividing 93 by 3 was, "You have 3 thirties in 90. Then, 1, 2, 3; so the answer is 31."

Throughout January and February, we varied math time to include only games on some days and only discussions on other days, but most days included both. This was a time when one child after another, almost daily, became able for the first time to attempt double-column addition and subtraction involving "regrouping," and they were succeeding in their attempts.

In March, the children were again eager to play games, especially Around the World, which was their favorite. Other frequently played games were *Shut the Box, Domicolor,* Four-in-a-Row, *Sorry* (modified as described in Kamii, 1985, p. 150), and *The Allowance Game.* The children also enjoyed making up their own versions of dominoes and games using the Hundred Board. During discussion time, they looked forward to the story problems I made up, and they frequently organized themselves into small groups to discuss the strategy that worked most quickly.

This trend continued for the final two months of school, with nearly all the pupils inventing really good games (such as Even Dominoes) and becoming adept at increasingly more difficult ones. The Spinner Game, a hard game, became a favorite for those who preferred a challenge. A memory I cherish is one of a visiting college math student playing the Spinner Game with three of my students. Because the children could add much faster than the adult, and because the visitor was amazed at their speed, the children rolled on the floor with laughter. Whenever visitors entered the room, the class liked to challenge them at addition problems. When an adult said, "I need paper and pencil to figure that out," one child had a crisp response: "We don't." Another child's response was, "That's the old-fashioned way."

THE THIRD AND FOURTH YEARS

The third and fourth years of teaching math without a textbook gave similar, positive results. Each class displayed a love of math that I had not seen during my first decade of teaching.

A technique that I began to use frequently during the third year was invitational teaching. Since not all children are interested in the same thing at the same time, I began to ask, for example, "Who would like to learn how to tell time?" or, "Who would like to stay with me to work on subtraction?" Children *want to* become competent when we respect their individuality and do not try to force them into a mold. I often worked with small groups, while the rest of the class played games.

CONCLUSION

As I look back, I am somewhat amazed at and yet proud of my metamorphosis. I had never given children credit for being smart enough to invent solutions. It took a lot of extra effort as a teacher to listen to what they were trying to say, and a lot of self-control to squelch the urge to take the fast-and-easy way of imposing my adult views and methods. But there was so much that never needed to be taught, because the children invented all kinds of things that had not even occurred to me. During math, I now see excitement, enthusiasm, and concentration on the children's faces. I hear voices coming from children who are self-assured, rarely timid, and quiet only while thinking.

I find myself wondering how teachers can go on depending on workbooks and drill sheets. But I also recall how skeptical and unsure I was at first of not showing the children how to solve a problem the "right" way. I now know, as can be seen in Chapter 10, that these children have developed as far as, and further than, the textbook would have taken them. I am firmly convinced that the great majority learned what no book of drills could have taught them: How to think.

CHAPTER 10

Evaluation

The way in which we evaluate a program or the progress of individual children depends not only on the specific abilities we assess but also on the theoretical framework within which we work. Different theories concerning children's thinking and learning lead to the conceptualization of different goals and objectives, different methods of teaching, and different methods and criteria of evaluation.

In arithmetic, a major objective of traditional instruction is to get children to learn correct *techniques* of producing right answers. In the Piagetian framework, by contrast, the objectives are conceived in terms of children's ability to think, that is, their capacity to invent various ways of solving problems and to judge which procedures and answers make sense. We do not stress the correctness of the answer, because if children can think, they *will* eventually get the correct answer.

The only thing that counts in standardized achievement tests is correct answers. These tests thus merely tell us how many correct answers a child produced (raw score) and how this raw score compares with those of his or her peers (percentile rank). They give no information about how the child arrived at the answers or whether he or she understood why those answers were correct.

In addition, because traditional math educators have not distinguished between logico-mathematical knowledge and social knowledge, major portions of standardized tests deal with aspects of arithmetical knowledge which are social and conventional in nature. Examples of social knowledge tapped by achievement tests include understanding the meaning of conventional forms such as the "is less than" sign ($<$), and knowing whether "one hundred and eighteen" is written 10018, 118, or 180. The Egyptians and Romans had conventions different from ours for writing these ideas, but their logico-mathematical knowledge was the same as ours.

Missing addends such as $3 + \underline{\hspace{1cm}} = 5$ are examples of how different theories lead to the conceptualization of different objectives and criteria of evaluation. Missing addends are generally taught in the first two grades, and they appear on the first two grade levels of standardized achievement tests. On the basis of Piaget's theory, however, I would neither teach missing addends nor test children on this topic. The reason is that all first graders demonstrate the logico-mathematical knowledge necessary to solve problems such as $3 +$ _____ $= 5$ in card games like Piggy Bank.[1] If a first grader has a 3 card in her hand and the rule says that she must make 5 with two cards, she will know that she needs a 2 card. But writing this knowledge down in conventional missing-addend form (social knowledge) is another matter.

We found out at Hall-Kent School that, if we never teach missing addends in first grade, about half of the children write the correct answer anyway to questions such as $3 +$ _____ $= 5$. If we never teach missing addends in second grade, either, almost all the children write the correct answer. The reason for this phenomenon is that, before their thought becomes reversible, young children *read* $3 +$ _____ $= 5$ as "3, 5." They therefore add the two numbers and write 8 in the blank space. When their thought becomes reversible, the children read the question in the same way adults do. (More details about this explanation can be found in Kamii, 1985, pp. 81–83).

In this chapter on evaluation, I will follow the sequence of goals and objectives that I have set out for my approach to math instruction, as discussed in Part II. Thus, the chapter is divided into sections on autonomy, place value, double-column addition, and problem solving. I conclude with a discussion of the evaluation of individual children's progress.

Throughout, I will be comparing the performance of second graders at Hall-Kent School with that of their peers in a school where the traditional math program was followed. The general picture that will emerge is that the performance of second graders at Hall-Kent School was about the same on the Stanford Achievement Test as that of traditionally instructed children. However, when given tests that probed into children's ability to think, the Hall-Kent children performed better.

The data presented in this chapter, which were collected in April and May of 1988, came from the following sources:

---

[1]Piggy Bank is played in a way similar to Find Ten, which was presented earlier (p. 104). Thirty-two cards are used, eight each of cards showing 1 penny (self-adhesive disk), 2 pennies, 3 pennies, and 4 pennies. The players can take cards only in pairs that make 5 (1 + 4, or 2 + 3). All the cards are dealt. Each player puts all the cards received in a pile, face down, without looking at them. When his turn comes, each player turns up the top card of his pile and tries to make 5 with two cards. Since the first player can never find two cards, he has to discard his card in the middle of the table, face up. If this card is a 3, and the next player turns over a 2, she can take the two cards and keep them. If, on the other hand, she

1. The routinely administered Stanford Achievement Test (SAT); raw scores on three content clusters were analyzed, namely, Place Value, Addition with Whole Numbers, and Problem Solving
2. Videotaped individual interviews in which we examined children's understanding of place value and double-column addition and their handling of misaligned digits in the following problem:

$$4$$
$$35$$
$$+\,24$$

3. The 1988 Math Sampler, a test we invented and administered to entire classes, consisting of problems in estimation and mental arithmetic as well as story problems. This test was a paper-and pencil test, but, instead of choosing from several possible answers printed on the test booklet, the children wrote their own computations and answers in the large, blank spaces provided.

We also had SAT scores for the previous year at Hall-Kent School, (from tests administered in April 1987). The second grade had a mean SAT Total Mathematics score of 73 (percentile), while the corresponding percentiles at the other schools were 85 or ábove. In 1988, the mean SAT Total Mathematics scores (percentiles) for the second grade were 79 at Hall-Kent School and 85 or above at the other schools.

All the subjects involved in this evaluation belonged to four second-grade classes—two classes at Hall-Kent School and two classes in two nearby, suburban, middle- to upper-middle-class schools known to produce high test scores. The socioeconomic level of the comparison group was slightly higher than that of our Hall-Kent sample, but we had to accept this factor because there is no school in the same area that is at the same socioeconomic level. We thus evaluated the effects of our constructivist program by comparing the performance of Hall-Kent children with that of children attending other schools in higher socioeconomic neighborhoods who receive traditional math instruction. The two groups will hereafter be referred to as the constructivist group ($n = 46$) and the traditional group ($n = 41$). The tables discussed later do not always include the same numbers of children because some were absent at the time the test was given.

---

turns over a 1 or a 4, she has to discard it in the middle of the table, face up. Play continues until all the cards have been used. The winner is the person who collected the greatest number of cards (or pairs of cards).

CHILDREN'S DEVELOPMENT OF AUTONOMY

It is very difficult to assess children's development of autonomy, as autonomy is complex and has many aspects. The only data we have collected so far are children's responses to question 5 on the 1988 Math Sampler: "There are 26 sheep and 10 goats on a ship. How old is the captain?" This is a question often mentioned at math conferences to illustrate the mindlessness resulting from traditional instruction. I had heard that many children gave the answer of 36, because 26 + 10 = 36!

Among our second-grade sample, 27% of the constructivist group wrote that this question did not make sense, but all of the traditionally instructed children wrote 36. The difference of 27 percentage points between the two groups is statistically significant ($p < .001$). Children at Hall-Kent School are taught to be critical and to speak up when an argument does not make sense. In traditional math education, by contrast, children are generally not encouraged to speak up when there is something they do not understand.

All the classes, both constructivist and traditional, reacted to this question with visible disturbance and puzzlement. When individual children raised their hands and asked questions during the test, we simply told them to think hard about the question and to put down the best answer they could. A few children at Hall-Kent School even loudly exclaimed, "It doesn't make sense!" but nevertheless wrote 36.

While the difference between the two groups may be statistically significant, this proportion is too low, from my point of view. There is clearly still ample room for improvement in the intellectual autonomy of Hall-Kent children.

PLACE VALUE

Stanford Achievement Test

The Place Value content cluster in the SAT taps mainly the social knowledge involved in place value rather than logico-mathematical knowledge. I will illustrate this with two sample test items I have made up that are similar to the actual items. In one item, pupils are shown an expanded form such as 500 + 20 + 0 and the following possible answers: 700, 520, 50020, and 5200. This is social knowledge because written numerals are made by conventions. The answer would be written DXX in Roman numerals. Another item shows a figure such as the example in Figure 10.1 and the following possible answers: 900, 216, 612, and 90.

Some of our children in the constructivist group find only 9 dots and say that the answer is not available, because they have never seen place-value boxes such as those in Figure 5.2. Place-value rules are made by convention. Roman numerals also have place-value rules, such as those involved in IV and VI, which are different from ours.

The mean raw scores for this cluster were 12.6 for the constructivist group and 14.64 for the traditional group. While the difference between the two groups is not statistically significant ($p < .10$), the traditional group performed better, near the maximum possible score of 15.

Individual Interviews

When the child came into the room for a videotaped individual interview, the interviewer first showed him or her a 3" × 5" card with the numeral 16 written on it and asked the child to count out 16 chips from a nearby pile. The interviewer then circled the 6 of 16 with the back of a pen and asked, "What does *this part* (the 6) mean? Could you show me with the chips what *this part* (the 6) means?" (No child has trouble showing 6 chips.)

The interviewer then circled the 1 of 16 and asked, "What about *this part* (the 1)? Could you show me with the chips what *this part* (the 1) means?" (Note the use of the term *this part* avoiding the use of any other word.) Almost all traditionally instructed second graders responded by showing only one chip.

The interviewer continued to probe: "You showed me all these chips (pointing out the 16 chips) for this number (circling the 16 on the card), and these (pointing to 6 chips) for this part (circling the 6 on the card), and this chip (pointing) for this part (circling the 1 on the card). What about the rest of the chips (pointing to the 9 or 10 chips that were not used)? Is this how it's supposed to be, or is there something strange here?" A few children replied that something was strange, but most of them said that they did not see anything wrong with what they had said.

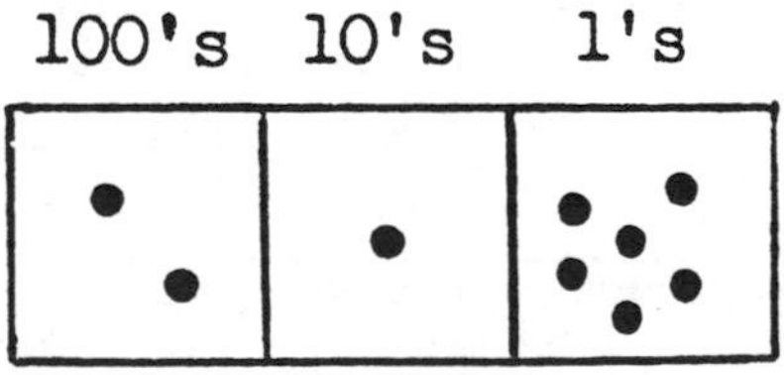

Figure 10.1. A figure typical of those shown in the SAT to assess children's knowledge of place value.

The children's responses were categorized into the following three groups:

1. The child showed 1 chip for the 1 in 16 and did not change his or her mind throughout the interview.
2. The child at first showed 1 chip for the 1 in 16 but changed his or her mind when questioned, and ended up showing 10 chips.
3. The child immediately showed 10 chips for the 1 in 16.

As can be seen in Table 10.1, 67% of the children in the constructivist group were found to be in the third category, while only 15% of the traditionally instructed second graders were. The difference between the two groups is statistically significant ($p < .001$).

Interpretation of Findings

Two points can be made about these findings. The first one is that there is a vast difference in the information provided by the SAT and by our interviews. The traditionally instructed group did very well on the SAT and came out slightly better than the constructivist group. In our interviews, however, only 15% of the traditional group was found to understand the meaning of the 1 in 16. The results of the two methods of evaluation are in marked contradiction.

These contradictory findings are due to the fact that the SAT taps mostly social knowledge, while our interviews tap mostly logico-mathematical knowledge. Whether through ignorance or indifference, test makers do not make a distinction between social knowledge and logico-mathematical knowledge; hence, they make tests that tap mostly social knowledge, which is superficial, easy to teach, and easy to measure. Logico-mathematical knowledge is much deeper, more complex, and harder to assess than social knowledge.

Teachers who follow traditional methods of instruction are usually shocked when they watch their children during a live interview or on videotapes afterward. Teachers conscientiously go through the lessons

TABLE 10.1: Understanding of Place Value of the
Constructivist and Traditional Groups
(by No. and Percentage of Children)

	n	Category 1	Category 2	Category 3
Constructivist	46	7 (15%)	8 (17%)	31 (67%)
Traditional	39	24 (62%)	9 (23%)	6 (15%)

$p < .001$

with bundles of straws, base-10 blocks, and/or workbooks and are at first incredulous when they see a child showing one chip for the 1 in 16. They teach within the empiricist framework, and their pupils look good on empiricist tests.

The second point to be made about the findings on children's understanding of place value is that, if children do not understand place value, they cannot be expected to understand double-column addition or any other operation with numbers greater than 10. This is the topic to which I now turn.

DOUBLE-COLUMN ADDITION INVOLVING "REGROUPING"

Stanford Achievement Test

The most specific information obtainable from the SAT was cluster scores, since item analyses were not made. The cluster that comes closest to showing children's knowledge of double-column addition is Addition with Whole Numbers. This cluster consists of 16 computational problems, some of which involve "regrouping."

The mean raw scores of the constructivist and traditional groups were about the same on this measure: 14.76 for the constructivist group and 15.12 for the traditional group. The maximum possible score is 16.

Individual Interviews

Children's Explanation of "Regrouping." For this part of the interview, the card and 16 chips used in the place-value task were left on the table, and the child was shown a 4″ × 6″ card on which the following problem was written:

$$16$$
$$+ 17$$

The interviewer asked the child to add these numbers mentally, give the answer, and then explain how he or she got the answer. Almost all the children in both groups gave the answer of 33. All the traditionally instructed children explained that they added the 6 and the 7 first. Almost all then said, "I put my 3 down here (pointing) and 1 up there, and 1 and 1 and 1 is 3; so I put 3 down here, and the answer is 33." By contrast, almost all the children in the constructivist group started by adding the tens first and proceeded in the ways described in Chapters 5 and 6.

The interviewer then took out another 3" × 5" card on which the numeral 17 had been written, and asked the child to count out 17 chips. When the child finished, the interviewer arranged all three cards and the two piles of chips as shown in Figure 10.2a, and pointed out the correspondence between the numeral 16 on the cards and the 16 chips, and between the numeral 17 on the cards and the 17 chips. The next request was for the child to explain, using the chips, how he or she arrived at the answer.

The children's responses were categorized into the following three groups:

1. The child could not explain by using chips the description of "regrouping" given verbally before. The children in this category showed their confusion in a surprisingly wide variety of ways, but two common attempts at explanations were as follows:
   a. "I take 6 from 16, and 7 from 17, and that makes 13. I then take 1 from the 13 and 1 and 1 [taken from one of the piles of 10; see Figure 10.2b], and that's how I got my answer." The interviewer protested, "I don't see 33 anywhere, and I don't understand how you got 33 with what you have here." Some children then put two sets of 3 more chips out, as shown in Figure 10.2c, to express the written convention with chips.
   b. The other common explanation is illustrated in Figure 10.2d. The child here demonstrated 6 + 7 in the same way as in the example just described. However, he "carried the 1" (moved 1 chip) from the pile of 13, placing it above the two heaps of 10, and got stuck. The children who remained stuck at this point were placed in category 1. Those who figured out the reasoning involved in "regrouping" at this point were placed in category 2.
2. The child could not explain "regrouping" using chips on his or her own but succeeded later as a result of the interviewer's probe, as just explained.
3. The child explained "regrouping" with perfect clarity. The traditionally instructed children started with 6 + 7 and made a pile of 13 chips. They then took 10 out of the 13 and put them together with the two other heaps of 10. The children in the constructivist group, on the other hand, started with 10 + 10, often showed that 7 + 3 made another 10, and that there were thus 30 and 3.

It can be seen in Table 10.2 that 83% of the constructivist group and 23% of the traditional group were able to explain "regrouping" using chips ($p < .001$).

Figure 10.2.   Unsuccessful attempts at explaining "regrouping" in addition, using chips.

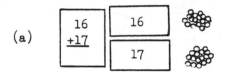

(a)

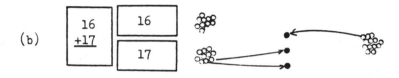

(b)

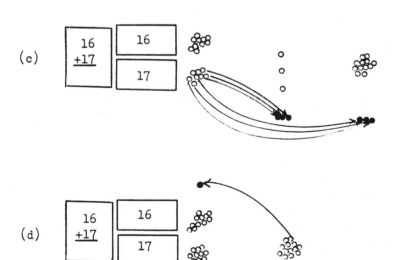

(c)

(d)

TABLE 10.2: Understanding of "Regrouping" by the
Constructivist and Traditional Groups
(by No. and Percentage of Children)

	n	Category 1	Category 2	Category 3
Constructivist	46	5 (11%)	3 (7%)	38 (83%)
Traditional	39	27 (69%)	3 (8%)	9 (23%)

p<.001

Children's Handling of Misaligned Digits. In the final part of the interview, we handed a sheet of paper to the child on which the following problem appeared:

$$4$$
$$35$$
$$+24$$

Following Labinowicz (1985, p. 323), whose technique we adapted, the interviewer asked the child to "read these numbers" and then to write the answer. When the child finished, the interviewer asked him or her to read the answer aloud and then inquired, "Does that sound right?"

The proportion who wrote 99 by mechanically following the rule of adding the columns was 11% for the constructivist group and 79% for the traditionally instructed group ($p < .001$).

Interpretation of Findings on SAT and in Interviews

The contrast between the information provided by the SAT and by our interviews is again striking. On the achievement test, the two groups appeared to be almost identical; however, in the interviews, the constructivist group performed far better. This contradiction again illustrates how different theories lead to different methods of and criteria for evaluating children's learning. For traditional math educators, the goal is for children to learn "facts" and rules (algorithms) to get answers, and the only thing that counts on achievement tests is the correctness of the answer. For constructivists, by contrast, the important thing is children's thinking. The Hall-Kent children demonstrated in the interviews that they understood the procedures they had invented. The traditionally instructed children demonstrated, on the other hand, that they had not understood the explanation of "regrouping" that had been taught.

The matrices in Table 10.3 show the relationship between children's understanding of place value and their understanding of "regrouping," for each of the two groups. It can be seen in these matrices that the propor-

TABLE 10.3: Relationship between Understanding of Place Value and of "Regrouping," for the Constructivist and Traditional Groups (by Number and Percentage of Children)

	"Regrouping" categories				"Regrouping" categories		
Place-value categories	1	2	3	Place-value categories	1	2	3
1	4(9%)	1(2%)	2(4%)	1	23(59%)		1(3%)
2		1(2%)	7(15%)	2	3(8%)	1(3%)	5(13%)
3	1(2%)	1(2%)	29(63%)	3	1(3%)	2(5%)	3(8%)
Constructivist Group (n=46)				Traditional Group (n=39)			

tion of children who understood both—that is, who fell into the third category on both dimensions—was 63% for the constructivist group and 8% for the traditional group ($p < .001$).

The 1988 Math Sampler

Estimation. The 1988 Math Sampler included four items of estimation that were presented for a limited time with the use of an overhead projector. Since none of the four groups had had any experience with such a timed test, we explained what was meant by estimation and gave two examples. After asking volunteers to say what their estimates were, we encouraged children to exchange ideas about different ways in which they had thought to arrive at a reasonable estimate. When the children understood the task, we demonstrated that they would have only 4.5 seconds to look at the problem and would have the same amount of time to write the answer. The specific problems are shown in Table 10.4. Only the first problem, 98 + 43, was given in multiple-choice format.

It can be observed in this table that the constructivist group did better than the traditional group on all the estimation items, and that the differences are statistically significant most of the time. These findings are not surprising, because the Hall-Kent children add the tens first when there are two digits, and the hundreds first when there are three digits.

TABLE 10.4:   Performance on Problems in Estimation,
Mental Arithmetic, and Written Arithmetic

Problems and Responses	Cons.* n=42	Trad.* n=41	Signif.
Estimation problems:			
98 + 43			
Chose "about 140"**	69	46	.02
347 + 282			
Wrote number in 500–700 range	64	39	.01
Wrote 629	7	0	.05
4 x 27			
Wrote number in 80–110 range	48	32	n.s.
Wrote 108	10	0	.02
$3.49 + $2.75			
Wrote number in $5–$7 range	71	61	n.s.
Mental arithmetic problems:			
98 + 43	48	17	.002
3 x 31 (31 + 31 + 31)	60***	17	.001
4 x 27 (27 + 27 = 54, 54 + 54 =108)	29	05	.002
Written arithmetic problem:			
49			
56			
62			
+88	48	32	n.s.

*Percentage giving correct answer or answer shown.

**The choices were "about 110," "about 140," "about 170," and "I have no idea."

***The percentage of third graders in the Fourth NAEP who gave the correct answer in written arithmetic was 56 (Kouba et al., 1988, p. 15). Without using pencils, the constructivist second graders did better than the third graders in the NAEP who used pencils.

The Stanford Achievement Test does not have a single question asking for an estimation. The only thing that counts on achievement tests is precise, correct answers. Because their theory does not recognize the importance of being able to get "ballpark" figures, they leave this ability completely out of their evaluation.

Precise, correct answers for $347 + 282$ and 4×27 were written in 4.5 seconds by 7% and 10%, respectively, of the constructivist group. By contrast, none of the children in the traditional group got correct answers in 4.5 seconds, and the differences are statistically significant ($p < .05$ and $p < .02$, respectively). This adds weight to my statement in an earlier chapter that many second graders at Hall-Kent School add big numbers faster than most adults.

Mental Arithmetic. We also used the overhead projector for mental arithmetic and limited the exposure time to 9 seconds. As can be seen in Table 10.4, significantly higher percentages of the constructivist group wrote correct answers to all three of the mental-arithmetic questions, compared to the traditional group. These findings are not surprising, in view of the fact that the children at Hall-Kent School hardly ever write anything in class and, instead, *think* and exchange ideas about what they think. The emphasis in traditional instruction, by contrast, is on *writing* in workbooks.

It must be pointed out that the Stanford Achievement Test does not have a single question in mental arithmetic and therefore does not tell us whether or not children can add two-digit numbers without writing anything down. The absence of both estimation and mental arithmetic is a serious flaw of the SAT.

Finally, it is significant to note in Table 10.4 that only 17% of the traditionally instructed children got the correct answer to $98 + 43$. Children accustomed to adding in their heads frequently change such a problem to $100 + 41$, and this, I believe, accounts for the higher percentage of Hall-Kent students giving the correct answer. This is another example of how different theories give rise to different methods of evaluation.

Written Arithmetic. The last item on the 1988 Math Sampler was the addition of the four numbers that can be seen at the bottom of Table 10.4. This untimed item was adapted from the Fourth National Assessment of Educational Progress (Kouba et al., 1988, p. 15), which found that only 48% of third graders got the correct answer to this kind of problem involving 4 two-digit numbers.

It can be seen in Table 10.4 that exactly the same percentage of second graders at Hall-Kent School got the correct answer as the third graders in the national assessment (48%). This percentage is slightly higher than that of the traditionally instructed second graders (32%). While this difference is not statistically significant, it is important to note that the children in the constructivist group wrote very little but that the traditional group wrote a great deal. Practice in writing does not necessarily result in children's ability to compute accurately with pencil and paper.

PROBLEM SOLVING (STORY PROBLEMS)

Stanford Achievement Test

The SAT has a cluster of items of the story-problem type, and the two groups' scores on this test were nearly identical. The mean raw score on Problem Solving was 12.62 for the constructivist group and 12.76 for the traditional group, with the maximum possible score for this cluster being 15.

The 1988 Math Sampler

The story-problem part of the 1988 Math Sampler consisted of eight problems. They were given first in the test, before the part involving estimation, mental arithmetic, and written computation, because some children become upset by timed tests.

The eight questions were made up mostly on the basis of findings from the National Assessment of Educational Progress (NAEP), because of the norms available on third graders as well as other age groups. Question 1 was adapted from the third NAEP (Lindquist, Carpenter, Silver, & Matthews, 1983). Questions 2–4, 6, and 8 were derived from the fourth NAEP (Kouba et al., 1988). Question 5, as noted earlier, has made the rounds at math conferences; and question 7 was our own invention.

In this test, each question was read aloud while the children silently read it in their booklets. We avoided the multiple-choice format because we wanted to know the ideas that came out of the children's heads as well as their process of thinking. Below each question was a space designated for the answer and ample room to write whatever children needed to write to figure out the answer. Most of the children had plenty of time to complete the test, which took about 40 minutes all together.

Table 10.5 summarizes our findings about children's performance on story problems. The first column of percentages gives the findings for third graders on the fourth NAEP (Kouba et al., 1988). It can be seen that the second graders in our constructivist group did better than the third graders on three of the four items for which national norms were

TABLE 10.5: Comparison of Performance of Constructivist, Traditional, and Grade-3 Norm Groups on
1988 Math Sampler Story Problems (Percentages)

Response	Grade 3* (NAEP)**	Grade 2		
		Const.* n=41	Tradit.* n=41	Signif. Diff.
1. 10 cars		61	29	32	.002
2. 65¢	58	93	83	10	n.s.
3. 28 children	56	61	51	10	n.s.
4. 6¢	29	56	29	27	.007
59 − 35 = 24¢ (±2)		5	24	19	.01
35 − 59		0	7	7	.05
5. It does not make sense.		27	0	27	.001
36		68	88	20	.02
6. 92 cookies		61	49	12	n.s.
Evidence of correct logic		78	54	24	.02
4 + 23 = 27		05	17	12	.05
7. 294 labels		20	02	18	.004
Evidence of correct logic		83	29	54	.001
21 + 14 = 35		10	29	19	.02
21 x 14 = 24		0	12	12	.02
8. $2.40	59	37	15	22	.02
Gobstoppers: 50¢		44	29	15	n.s.
Lifesavers: 90¢		51	34	17	n.s.
Tootsie Pops: $1		44	29	15	n.s.

*Percentage giving answer shown.
**These are the results from the Fourth NAEP (Kouba
et al., 1988).

available. The traditionally instructed second graders in Alabama did as
well as or better than the third graders on two of the items and did less
well on the other two.

Let us go on to compare the second graders at Hall-Kent School with
the traditionally instructed second graders. I will present each question
in turn and discuss the results. As we shall see, the constructivist group
did better than the traditional group on all the items, especially the more
difficult ones.

Question 1. There are 49 children who want to go to the zoo. Some of
their parents are willing to drive their cars and can take 5 children in

each car. How many cars will be needed to take all 49 children to the zoo?

This question was adapted from one on the third NAEP: "An army bus holds 36 soldiers. If 1,128 soldiers are being bussed to their training site, how many buses are needed?" (Lindquist et al., 1983, p. 18). Only 24% of the 13-year-olds in the third NAEP answered this question correctly, and 47% said 31, 31.33, 31⅓, and so on. So, we felt that we needed to simplify our question for second graders.

This is a division problem, which many second graders tackled by repeated addition of 5. Twice as many children in the constructivist group (61%) gave the correct answer of 10 cars as in the traditional group (29%), a statistically significant difference.

Only 10% in each group said that 9 cars would be needed, and no one wrote "9 R 4" or "9⅘." Second graders have not yet received instruction on remainders, fractions, and decimal fractions, and have not yet learned to work mindlessly on this kind of problem, like the 13-year-olds in the third NAEP.

In the traditional group there were 17% who wrote answers close to 10. Ten percent wrote 8, 2% wrote 11, and 5% wrote 12. Because these answers are almost correct, it can be assumed that these children's logic was probably correct and that their errors were probably computational.

Two errors in logic were found fairly frequently in both groups: $49 - 5 = 44 \ (\pm 1)$, which was found once (2%) in the constructivist group and 3 times (7%) in the traditional group; and $49 + 5 = 54 \ (\pm 2)$, which was found 4 times (10%) in the constructivist group and 5 times (12%) in the traditional group. The children who gave the latter response obviously did not think that there should be fewer cars than children.

A disadvantage of administering a group test such as this is that if children write only their answers, without showing their computations, it is impossible to understand how they arrived at their answers. When they do write something, however, it is possible to evaluate their process of reasoning. For example, one child in the constructivist group gave 17 as his answer and had written, "5, 10, 15, 20, 25, 30, 35, 40, 41, 42, 43, 44, 45, 46, 47, 48, 49," for a total of 17 numbers. This is not a serious error compared to the following examples found in the traditional group:

• One child gave 6 as her answer, but below it she had written

$$
\begin{array}{cc}
\begin{array}{r}
1 \\
49 \\
+\ 5 \\
\hline
54
\end{array}
&
\begin{array}{r}
49 \\
-\ 5 \\
\hline
44
\end{array}
\end{array}
$$

• One child gave 20 as her answer, but below it she had written

$$
\begin{array}{r}
49 \\
-\ 5 \\
\hline 44
\end{array}
\qquad
\begin{array}{r}
49 \\
\times\ 5 \\
\hline 20
\end{array}
$$

(These children remind us of those who ask, "Do I add or subtract now? Or maybe I need to multiply.")
• One child gave 49 + 5 as her answer but crossed it out and wrote 13.
• One child wrote 4 as her answer, but below it she had written

$$
\begin{array}{r}
49 \\
-5 \\
\hline 19
\end{array}
\qquad
\begin{array}{r}
19 \\
-\ 5 \\
\hline 15
\end{array}
\qquad
\begin{array}{r}
15 \\
-\ 5 \\
\hline 10
\end{array}
\qquad
\begin{array}{r}
10 \\
-\ 5 \\
\hline 5
\end{array}
$$

• One child wrote 10 as her answer but had written

$$
\begin{array}{r}
49 \\
-5 \\
\hline 19
\end{array}
\qquad
\begin{array}{r}
9 \\
+\ 1 \\
\hline 10
\end{array}
$$

(This was nonetheless counted as a correct answer in the data analysis.)
My conclusion from this analysis of errors is that, while there are similarities between the two groups, the children in the constructivist group made fewer errors in reasoning. Only 12% of the constructivist group did either 49 + 5 or 49 − 5. By contrast, 19% of the traditionally instructed group did either 49 + 5 or 49 − 5, and others did a large variety of things that did not make sense.

Children can use their natural intelligence to solve this problem without ever going to school. The child in the constructivist group who got the correct answer by drawing sticks in boxes, as shown in Figure 10.3, is an example of this statement. The conclusion from the preceding analysis is that, if the children in the constructivist group did not get the correct answer, they were at least relatively free of nonsense. I wonder whether the children in the traditional group might have done better on this item if they had not been instructed to follow rules of place value, double-column addition, and double-column subtraction that they did not understand.

Question 2. At the store, a package of filler paper costs 30¢, a roll of tape costs 35¢, and a set of erasers costs 20¢. What is the cost of a roll of tape and a package of filler paper?

Figure 10.3. One child's way
of doing 49 ÷ 5.

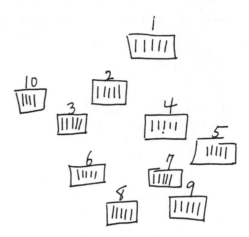

The question on the fourth NAEP was similar to the following: "At the store, a package of screws costs 30¢, a roll of tape costs 35¢, and a box of nails costs 20¢. What is the cost of a roll of tape and a package of screws?" (Kouba et al., 1988, p. 18). The questions that actually appeared in the test, by law, cannot be published. The authors reporting the results of the NAEP, therefore, have to make up items similar to those that were used in the test.

Our question turned out to be very easy for both groups, and 93% and 83% respectively gave the correct answer of 65¢. The proportion who answered 85¢ was only 5% of the constructivist group and 12% of the traditional group. These differences between the two groups are not significant.

Question 3. There were 31 children in the class at the beginning of the year. Six moved away but 3 moved into town and are new in the class. How many children are in the class now?

The question was adapted from the one made up for publication of the results of the fourth NAEP: "There are 31 birds on a fence. Six take off and 3 more land. How many birds are on the fence then?" (Kouba et al., 1988, p. 18).

Our question involved only addition and subtraction of small numbers and yielded only a very small difference between the two groups. The wrong answers were mainly of two kinds: being off by 1 (writing either 27 or 29), which accounted for 12% of the constructivist group and 17% of the traditional group; and answering 34 (±1) (for 31 + 3), which accounted for 10% of the constructivist group and 20% of the traditional group.

Question 4. Chris buys a Coke for 35¢ and French fries for 59¢. How much change does she get back from a dollar? This question was adapted from the following one on the fourth NAEP: "Chris buys a pencil for 35¢ and a soda for 59¢. How much change does she get back from $1.00?" (Kouba et al., 1988, p. 18).

Our question was answered correctly by 56% of our constructivist group and 29% of our traditional group, and the difference is significant. Only one child wrote 94¢, and 10% of each group wrote either 84¢ (for 59 + 35) or 16 (for $1.00 − 84¢).

The error most frequently made by the traditional group (24%) was giving the answer 24¢ (59 − 35). This is clearly an error in logic committed by children who are not using their natural intelligence. An even worse error found only in the traditional group (7%) was 35 − 59, written vertically, with answers of 86, 16, and 76.

The other wrong answers, such as 36, 40, and 50 without anything else on paper, are impossible to explain. In the future, it will be worth interviewing all the children who write answers that are impossible to interpret. Combining a group test such as this with individual interviews will provide much more information efficiently.

A surprising number of children in the traditionally instructed group subtracted 35 from 59, or 59 from 35. The significance of the findings from question 4 is not just that the constructivist group did better but that 31% of the traditionally instructed group, compared to 5% of the constructivist group, subtracted one price from another, a procedure that can be characterized only as nonsense.

Question 5. Table 10.5 shows the results; however, since question 5 has already been discussed in this chapter, in the section on autonomy, I will go on to question 6.

Question 6. The teacher brought 4 boxes of cookies. There are 23 cookies in each box. How many cookies are there to share all together?

The question on the fourth NAEP that inspired this one was: "Pam has 4 pictures. There are 3 trees and 5 cars in each picture. Which number sentence gives the total number of cars in the pictures?" (Kouba et al., 1988, p. 18). The choices given were: 4 + 5, 4 × 3, 4 × 5, and 4 + 3 + 5.

It is interesting to note that, for our question, no statistically significant difference was found when the percentages of correct answers were compared. However, when the category of "correct answer" was enlarged to include those who showed evidence of correct logic, the proportions changed to 78% (constructivist) and 54% (traditional), a significant difference. An example of evidence of correct logic is the number 23 written four times, even if the answer given is 52.

A fairly frequently found error in logic was 27 (for 4 + 23), found among 17% of the traditionally instructed group and 5% of the constructivist group, a statistically significant difference.

Question 7. There are 21 children in the class. If they each bring 14 soup labels, how many labels will there be all together?

This is a harder multiplication problem we made up because the preceding one seemed too easy. Second graders who got the correct answer solved it by laborious, repeated addition. The correct answer of 294 was given by 20% of the constructivist group and 2% of the traditional group, a significant difference.

When the category of "correct answer" was enlarged to include the responses that demonstrated correct logic, the figures rose to 83% for the constructivist group and 29% for the traditional group, again a statistically significant difference. An example of a child who demonstrated correct logic is one who wrote 21 (approximately) 14 times, or wrote 14 (approximately) 21 times without necessarily getting the correct answer. The difference between the two groups—54 percentage points—is dramatic and is the largest difference found in the column of differences between the two groups.

It must be noted that the proportion of children who demonstrated correct logic increased slightly from question 6 to question 7 in the constructivist group, but decreased in the traditional group from 54% to 29%. I expected the computation to be much harder in question 7 but did not expect the logic of multiplication or repeated addition to decrease so dramatically in the traditional group.

The answer of 35, resulting from the addition of 21 children and 14 labels, was found among 10% of the constructivist group and 29% of the traditional group. The difference between these proportions is significant, and the high percentage of this answer in the traditional group is distressing.

The answer of 24 was found only in the traditional group (12%) and was obtained with the following procedure:

$$
\begin{array}{r}
21 \\
\times\ 14 \\
\hline
24
\end{array}
$$

The children obtaining this answer multiplied each column separately and then placed the two answers next to each other. This demonstrated how children who are taught incomprehensible rules invent other similar rules, instead of thinking whether the answer can be 24 if 21 children each bring 14 labels.

Question 8. Pete bought 6 candy Gobstoppers, 3 rolls of Lifesavers, and 8 Tootsie Pops. How much did Pete spend? [The following prices were given for each candy:]

Gobstoppers	Lifesavers	Tootsie Pops
3 for 25¢	1 roll 30¢	4 for 50¢

The corresponding question on the fourth NAEP was: "Pete bought 6 stamps (3 for 25¢), 3 rings (1 for 30¢), and 8 pins (4 for 50¢). About how much did Pete send?" (Kouba et al., 1988, p. 18).

The correct answer to our question, $2.40, was obtained by 37% of the constructivist group and 15% of the traditional group. The difference of 22 percentage points is significant.

The percentages who wrote correct answers for parts of the question (50¢, 90¢, and $1.00) were likewise higher in the constructivist group; however, the differences are not significant.

Interpretation of Findings

Our story problems are a far cry from those of the Stanford Achievement Test. The problems on the latter are very easy; a typical example, of my own composing, is as follows:

Johnny bought 14 oranges and gave 5 of them to Suzie. How many does he have left?

Another type of problem on this test taps the child's social knowledge and could read like this:

Suzie had 4 stickers. She got 9 more. Which number sentence can you use to find how many stickers she has all together: 9 − 4 = _____ , 4 + 9 = _____ , or _____ + 4 = 9?

The easy and superficial problems of the SAT and the resultant low "ceiling" explain why the constructivist group did not perform differently from the traditional group on this test. Our test, by contrast, required reasoning and gave the constructivist group a chance to reveal its strengths.

Evaluators traditionally compare only the numbers or proportions of correct answers given by various groups. A more informative approach, from the standpoint of seeking educational implications, may be a comparison of the wrong answers children give. Examples of faulty reasoning were found in both groups, but the quantity and variety of illogical reasoning found in the traditional group were significantly greater. Traditional instruction results in the well-known "dance of the digits." In speculating about the future of these children, I would say that those who were encouraged to think in their own ways have a better chance of becoming able to think correctly than those who followed rules for making digits dance.

INDIVIDUAL CHILDREN'S PROGRESS

The kinds of testing we have discussed so far in this chapter have dealt with the evaluation of a program, as reflected in the test scores of groups of children. It is necessary also to evaluate individual children's progress, for purposes of accountability and informing parents.

As anyone who has experience with this process knows all too well, standardized achievement tests are now indiscriminately used to evaluate everything from individual teachers and children to schools and school systems. From my point of view, this is a grave error. I believe that we must use many different kinds of tests and take care that the ones we choose serve our different purposes in testing.

For the evaluation of individual children's learning, the important thing to assess is *each child's progress over time*. The current practice in many states is to determine the child's percentile rank or stanine, instead. The main problem with this practice, esp cially in the primary grades, is that a number expressing a child's rank in a group tells us nothing about a child's learning. If we want to assess children's progress, we have to assess what they knew and did not know at one time and compare this with their knowledge at a subsequent time.

Table 10.6 shows part of an evaluation of children's progress in mental arithmetic, conducted in Linda Joseph's class. The items in the left-hand column of this table are those of a test that I made up with a graduate student. This test consists of computational problems of various kinds. In individual interviews, the child was given two sheets of paper, one at a time, on which these problems appeared. The child was asked to slide a ruler down the page as he or she answered one question orally and went on to the next one. The examiner had a form, took notes, and asked questions when necessary.

The numbers 1 through 10 across the top of Table 10.6 stand for individual children. The 10 children were chosen to represent both extremes of competence in the class, as well as the middle. Each child is represented once in September and again in April/May of the same school year.

The plus signs in the body of the table represent the occasions when the children gave correct answers to the various problems on the test, under the conditions specified.

The last column of Table 10.6 shows the percentage of the entire class who passed each item in April/May. These percentages can be very useful to teachers as they set goals for the year. We can see from this column that double-column subtraction involving "regrouping" was harder for these children than some multiplication problems.

The +'s on the first page of Table 10.6 represent the correct answers each child gave within 5 seconds to single-digit addition and subtraction problems. The purpose of this part of the assessment was to find out about the child's construction of the network of numerical relationships, as discussed in Chapter 5.

It can be seen from this part of the test that the child who performed the best in the spring, child 1, already had an elaborate network of numerical relationships at the beginning of the year. By contrast, child 10, the one who was last in the rank order at the end of the year, was also the least advanced child in September. While child 10 did not perform very well at the end of the year, he did make considerable progress over the year. Although he still could not use any doubles (such as 3 + 3) in problems such as 3 + 4 in the spring, he seems by that time to have constructed all the doubles themselves. He also showed evidence of beginning to use combinations that make 10. For example, he seems to have changed problems such as 8 + 4 to (8 + 2) + 2.

Data on the second part of this test concern addition, subtraction, and multiplication with two- or three-digit numbers. There was no time limit for inclusion of correct answers for the 17 problems in this part, and the plus signs represent correct answers arrived at in whatever way the child could think of. Some children counted up or down to do 13 + 8 and 27 − 8.

It can be seen from Table 10.6 that child 1 could do almost everything on this part of the test at the beginning of the school year. The only thing with which he had trouble in September was subtraction involving "regrouping." Although this test may give the impression that child 1 did not learn much in second grade, his progress was made in speed and in performing operations with three- and four-digit numbers. This was one of the children who got exact, correct answers to 347 + 282 and 4 × 27 in 4.5 seconds in the estimation test.

Trailing closest behind child 1 on this part of the September test were children 2 and 4. Child 2 passed all the items on this part in the spring. Child 3 actually ranked with these most advanced children, although not showing good results here. This was an example of "a bad day" for this child.

continued on page 184

TABLE 10.6: Second Graders' Performance in Mental Arithmetic

Test Problems	September										April/May											
	Child 1	Child 2	Child 3	Child 4	Child 5	Child 6	Child 7	Child 8	Child 9	Child 10	Child 1	Child 2	Child 3	Child 4	Child 5	Child 6	Child 7	Child 8	Child 9	Child 10	Class %
Addition, 1 digit																					
Doubles																					
4 + 4	+	+	+	+	+	+	+	+	+	+	+	+	+	+	+	+	+	+	+	+	100
6 + 6	+	+	+	+			+	+	+		+	+	+	+	+	+	+	+		+	96
9 + 9		+	+	+				+	+		+	+	+	+	+	+	+	+	+	+	87
8 + 8	+		+	+		+		+	+		+	+	+	+	+	+	+	+	+	+	96
7 + 7	+	+	+	+		+	+	+	+	+	+	+	+	+	+	+	+	+	+	+	92
10 combos																					
8 + 2	+	+	+	+	+	+	+	+	+	+	+	+	+	+	+	+	+	+	+	+	96
3 + 7	+	+	+	+	+	+	+	+	+	+	+	+	+	+	+	+	+	+	+	+	96
4 + 6	+	+	+	+	+	+	+	+		+	+	+	+	+	+	+	+	+	+	+	83
+2																					
2 + 6	+	+	+	+	+	+	+	+	+		+	+	+	+	+	+	+	+	+		87
Others																					
5 + 3	+	+	+	+	+	+	+	+			+	+	+	+	+	+	+	+	+	+	83
Using doubles																					
3 + 4	+	+	+	+		+	+	+	+		+	+	+	+	+	+	+	+	+	+	87
4 + 5	+	+	+	+		+	+	+	+		+	+	+	+	+	+	+	+	+		75
5 + 6	+	+	+	+		+	+	+			+		+	+	+	+		+	+		83
5 + 7	+	+	+	+			+	+			+		+	+	+	+		+			66
7 + 8		+	+	+				+			+		+	+	+	+		+	+	+	66

	%
Using 10 combos	
7 + 4	79
8 + 4	87
9 + 4	96
8 + 5	83
9 + 7	79
3 or more addends	
4+1+6	75
4+3+5	58
5+2+8	58
6	
3	
7	
+2	33
Subtraction, 1 digit	
Inverse of double	
12 – 6	75
Inverse of 10 combos	
10 – 8	83
10 – 6	83
Inverse of +2	
7 – 2	87

TABLE 10.6 (continued)

Addition, 2 or more digits	September										April/May										Class %
	Child 1	Child 2	Child 3	Child 4	Child 5	Child 6	Child 7	Child 8	Child 9	Child 10	Child 1	Child 2	Child 3	Child 4	Child 5	Child 6	Child 7	Child 8	Child 9	Child 10	
22 +7	+	+	+	+			+				+	+	+	+	+	+	+	+	+	+	92
28 +31	+	+	+	+				+	+		+	+	+	+	+	+	+	+		+	96
13 +8	+	+	+	+		+	+		+		+	+	+	+	+	+		+	+	+	92
27 +13	+	+		+								+	+	+	+	+	+	+			75
27 + 82	+	+	+	+							+	+	+	+	+	+	+	+			83
28 +72	+	+		+							+	+		+	+	+	+				71
254 +363	+										+	+		+	+	+	+				50

	46	42	33	79	62	62	79	71	87	71
448 +274	+									
7 52 +186	+	+								
7+52+186	+	+								
Subtraction, 2 digits										
48 -27				+						
27 - 8	+			+	+					
63 -24						+	+			
Multiplication										
3 x 7	+	+	+	+	+	+	+	+		
4 x 10	+	+	+	+	+	+	+	+		
3 x4	+	+	+	+	+	+	+	+	+	
10 x 4	+		+	+	+		+	+	+	+

At the end of the rank order on this part were children 9 and 10. Throughout the year, these children were not able to construct place value, and this was the reason for their low performance. It is noteworthy that child 9 often coped by drawing sticks. His performance on a task with misaligned numbers (not part of this test) is reproduced in Figure 10.4. He drew a line to indicate 24 and drew 11 more sticks to represent 35. He then went back to the first 24 sticks and used them to count on from 35, up to his marker for 24. He used his fingers to add 4 more and gave the answer of 62. While his answer is off by one, this is a much more intelligent procedure than adding the columns mechanically and writing 99. Incidentally, child 10, who had been coached at home, wrote 499 as the answer to this problem.

Child 5 "bloomed" during the year, as can be seen in Table 10.6, especially on the second part of the test. Her column for the second part was a total blank in September, but it was full of plus marks in April/May. We find children like her every year who show growth in spurts.

Children 6, 7, and 8 made average progress. They comfortably added two-digit numbers involving "regrouping" in April/May but were not as capable with three-digit numbers. They also had trouble with subtraction involving "regrouping."

This kind of evaluation seems much more informative to parents, teachers, and researchers than saying that in April child 10 was at the 25th percentile on Total Mathematics or on a content cluster within the SAT.

CONCLUSION

I would like to conclude with a word about achievement testing and accountability. Traditional, empiricist educators assume that the job of the teacher is to put knowledge into children's heads. They also assume that the proof of this transmission of knowledge is a high score on standardized tests. Both of these assumptions, as I believe this book has demonstrated, are erroneous and outdated.

Piaget proved scientifically, through more than half a century of research, that children construct logico-mathematical knowledge from within. All the teacher can do is to stimulate the child's own construction of this knowledge from the inside, in the ways described in this book. Children come to school with the intelligence given them by their parents, who supply both the heredity and the environment that explain intelligence.

It is much easier for teachers to give model procedures for children to

Figure 10.4. The tool invented by a child to add two-digit numbers without a system of tens.

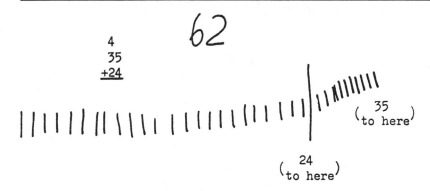

imitate than to encourage them to invent their own solutions. We have seen in this chapter, however, that the imposition of adult algorithms serves only to reinforce children's heteronomy and to hinder the development of their natural ability to think. Children 9 and 10 in Table 10.6 *will* eventually construct place value and double-column addition, if they are encouraged to use their own intelligence.

The National Council of Teachers of Mathematics (1988) is right in saying that it is imperative to develop new approaches to evaluation if better instructional practices are to become a reality. "Back-to-basics" and "test-mania," as tragic and distasteful as I find them, seem to be a necessary stage of American education. However, the next stage will not come all by itself. The arrival of the next stage depends on individuals who are willing to stand up and push education forward, instead of back to "basics."

If we really want independent, creative thinkers who have initiative, confidence, and moral autonomy, we must seriously foster these qualities, from the beginning of children's lives. What education needs is not higher test scores, but a fundamental reexamination of our goals and objectives, and of the ways in which we try to attain these goals.

APPENDIX
REFERENCES
INDEX
ABOUT THE AUTHOR

Resources

COMMERCIALLY MADE GAMES

Readers are referred to the next section for the catalogs mentioned here.

Addition and Subtraction Shapes. (1980). Leicester, England: Taskmaster. (Listed in Didax catalog.)

The Allowance Game. (1984). Carson, CA: Lakeshore Curriculum Materials. (Listed in Toys to Grow On catalog.)

Always 12 (in English); *Die Verflixte 12* (in German); *Toujours 12* (in French). (1979). West Germany: Ravensburger.

Boomerang. (1982). Paris: Jeux Nathan. (No longer available.)

Domicolor. (1984). West Germany: Ravensburger.

Dominique. (1980). Ronkonkoma, NY: Great Games.

Parcheesi. (1975). Bay Shore, NY: Selchow & Righter.

Regie (in German); *Passe Muraille* (in French). (1981). West Germany: Milton Bradley. (Not available in the United States.)

Shoot the Moon. (n.d.). Grand Rapids, MI: Wm. F. Drueke & Sons. (Listed in World Wide Games catalog.)

Shut the Box. (1984). Springfield, MA: Milton Bradley.

Sorry. (1972). Salem, MA: Parker Brothers.

Stack-Ominos. (1978). New York: Pressman.

Take Ten. (1975). D. N. Merom Hagalil, Israel: OrDa Industries. (Listed in Dale Seymour catalog.)

Tens and Twenties. (1981). Leicester, England: Taskmaster. (Listed in Didax catalog.)

Tiddly Winks. (1978). New York: Pressman.

Tri-Ominos. (1968). New York: Pressman. (Listed in Educational Teaching Aids catalog.)

Vagabondo. (1979). Leicester, England: Invicta. (No longer available.)

COMPANIES WITH MAIL-ORDER CATALOGS

The list of firms given here is intended to assist teachers in ordering some of the commercially made games and game equipment described in Chapter 8. The information presented was current when this book went to press.

Creative Publications, 5005 W. 110th Street, Oak Lawn, IL 60453
Cuisenaire Co. of America, 12 Church Street, Box D, New Rochelle, NY 10802
Didax Educational Resources, 5 Fourth Street, Peabody, MA 01960
Educational Teaching Aids, 199 Carpenter Avenue, Wheeling, IL 60090
The Paragon, Tom Harvey Road, Westerly, RI 02891
Dale Seymour Publications, P.O. Box 10888, Palo Alto, CA 94303
Toys to Grow On, P.O. Box 17, Long Beach, CA 90801
World Wide Games, Colchester, CT 06415

References

Abbott, J. S., & Wells, D. W. (1985). *Mathematics today*, Teacher's edition. Level 2, Mathematics today series. Orlando, FL: Harcourt Brace Jovanovich.

Bednarz, N., & Janvier, B. (1982). The understanding of numeration in primary school. *Educational studies in Mathematics, 13*, 33–57.

Bolster, L. C., Crown, W., Hamada, R., Hanson, V., Lindquist, M. M., McNerney, C., Nibbelink, W., Prigge, G., Rahlfs, C., Robitaille, D., Shultz, J., Sharron, S., Swafford, J., Vance, I., Williams, D. E., Wilson, J., & Wisner, R. (1987a). *Invitation to mathematics: 1*. Invitation to mathematics series. Glenview, IL: Scott, Foresman.

Bolster, L. C., Crown, W., Hamada, R., Hanson, V., Lindquist, M. M., McNerney, C., Nibbelink, W., Prigge, G., Rahlfs, C., Robitaille, D., Shultz, J., Sharron, S., Swafford, J., Vance, I., Williams, D. E., Wilson, J., & Wisner, R. (1987b). *Invitation to mathematics: 2*. Invitation to mathematics series. Glenview, IL: Scott, Foresman.

Carpenter, T. P., Corbitt, M. K., Kepner, H., Lindquist, M. M., & Reys, R. E. (1980). Results and implications of the second NAEP mathematics assessment: Elementary school. *Arithmetic Teacher, 27*(8), 10–12, 44–47.

Cauley, K. M. (1988). Construction of logical knowledge: Study of borrowing in subtraction. *Journal of Educational Psychology, 80*, 202–205.

Doise, W., & Mugny, G. (1984). *The social development of the intellect*. New York: Pergamon.

Flanders, J. R. (1987). How much of the content in mathematics textbooks is new? *Arithmetic Teacher, 35*(1), 18–23.

Gréco, P. (1962). Une recherche sur la commutativité de l'addition [Research on the commutativity of addition]. In P. Gréco & A. Morf (Eds.), *Structures numériques élémentaires* (pp. 151–227). Paris: Presses Universitaires de France.

Gréco, J., Grize, J.-B., Papert, S., & Piaget, J. (1960). *Problèmes de la construction du nombre*. Paris: Presses Universitaires de France.

Inhelder, B., & Piaget, J. (1963). De l'itération des actions à la récurrence élémentaire. In P. Gréco, B. Inhelder, B. Matalon, & J. Piaget (Eds.), *La formation des raisonnements récurrentiels* (pp. 47–120). Paris: Presses Universitaires de France.

Inhelder, B., & Piaget, J. (1964). *Early growth of logic in the child*. New York: Harper & Row. (Original work published 1959).

Kamii, C. (1982). *Number in preschool and kindergarten.* Washington, DC: National Association for the Education of Young Children.

Kamii, C. (1985). *Young children reinvent arithmetic.* New York: Teachers College Press.

Kamii, C. (1986). Place value: An explanation of its difficulty and educational implications for the primary grades. *Journal of Research in Childhood Education, 1,* 75–86.

Kamii, C., & DeVries, R. (1978). *Physical knowledge in preschool education.* Englewood Cliffs, NJ: Prentice-Hall.

Kamii, C., & DeVries, R. (1980). *Group games in early education.* Washington, DC: National Association for the Education of Young Children.

Kamii, C., & Knight, M. (1987). *Double-column addition: A teacher uses Piaget's theory* (videotape). NCTM and Teachers College Press.

Kamii, M. (1980, May). *Place value: Children's efforts to find a correspondence between digits and numbers of objects.* Paper presented at the tenth annual symposium of the Jean Piaget Society, Philadelphia.

Kamii, M. (1982). *Children's graphic representation of numerical concepts: A developmental study.* (Doctoral dissertation, Harvard University, 1982). *Dissertation Abstracts International, 43,* 1478A.

Kouba, V. L., Brown, C. A., Carpenter, T. P., Lindquist, M. M., Silver, E. A., & Swafford, J. O. (1988). Results of the fourth NAEP assessment of mathematics: Number, operations, and word problems. *Arithmetic Teacher, 35*(8), 14–19.

Labinowicz, E. (1985). *Learning from children: New Beginnings for Teaching Numerical Thinking.* Menlo Park, CA: Addison-Wesley.

Lindquist, M. M., Carpenter, T. P., Silver, E. A., & Matthews, W. (1983). The third national mathematics assessment: Results and implications for elementary and middle schools. *Arithmetic Teacher, 31*(4), 14–19.

Madell, R. (1985). Children's natural processes. *Arithmetic Teacher, 32*(7), 20–22.

National Council of Teachers of Mathematics. (1988, July). *Curriculum and evaluation standards for school mathematics* [draft]. Reston, VA: National Council of Teachers of Mathematics.

Perret-Clermont, A.-N. (1980). *Social interaction and cognitive development in children.* New York: Academic Press.

Piaget, J. (1950a). *Introduction à l'épistémologie génétique, Tome I: La pensée mathématique.* Paris: Presses Universitaires de France.

Piaget, J. (1950b). *Introduction à l'épistémologie génétique, Tome II: La pensée physique.* Paris: Presses Universitaires de France.

Piaget, J. (1950c). *Introduction à l'épistémologie génétique, Tome III: La pensée biologique et la pensée sociologique.* Paris: Presses Universitaires de France.

Piaget, J. (1954). *The construction of reality in the child.* New York: Basic Books. (Original work published 1937)

Piaget, J. (1965). *The moral judgment of the child.* New York: Free Press. (Original work published 1932)

Piaget, J. (1971). *Biology and knowledge.* Chicago: University of Chicago Press. (Original work published 1967)

Piaget, J. (1971). *The child's conception of time.* New York: Ballantine Books. (Original work published 1946)

Piaget, J. (1973). *To understand is to invent.* New York: Grossman. (Original work published 1948)

Piaget, J. (1980). Foreword. In C. Kamii & R. DeVries, *Group games in early education* (pp. vii). Washington, DC: National Association for the Education of Young Children.

Piaget, J., & Inhelder, B. (1967). *The child's conception of space.* New York: W. W. Norton. (Original work published 1948)

Piaget, J., & Inhelder, B. (1969). *The psychology of the child.* New York: Basic Books. (Original work published 1966)

Piaget, J., Inhelder, B., & Szeminska, A. (1960). *The child's conception of geometry.* London: Routledge and Kegan Paul. (Original work published 1948)

Piaget, J., & Szeminska, A. (1965). *The child's conception of number.* New York: W. W. Norton. (Original work published 1941)

Resnick, L. B. (1982). Syntax and semantics in learning to subtract. In T. P. Carpenter, J. M. Moser, & T. A. Romberg (Eds.), *Addition and subtraction: A cognitive perspective* (pp. 136–155). Hillsdale, NJ: Lawrence Erlbaum Associates.

Resnick, L. B. (1983). A developmental theory of number understanding. In H. P. Ginsburg (Ed.), *The development of mathematical thinking* (pp. 110–151). New York: Academic Press.

Ross, S. (1986, April). *The development of children's place-value numeration concepts in grades two through five.* Paper presented at the annual meeting of the American Educational Research Association, San Francisco. (ERIC Document Reproduction Service No. ED 273 482)

Silvern, S., & Kamii, C. (1988). Place value and commutativity: Their role in double-column addition. Unpublished manuscript.

Sinclair, A., Siegrist, F., & Sinclair, H. (1983). Young children's ideas about the written number system. In D. Rogers & J. A. Sloboda (Eds.), *The acquisition of symbolic skills* (pp. 535–542). New York and London: Plenum Press.

Thompson, C. S., & Rathmell, E. C. (1988). NCTM's standards for school mathematics, K–12. *Arithmetic Teacher, 35*(9), 17–19.

Index

About the Author

Constance Kamii is Professor in the School of Education at the University of Alabama at Birmingham. She previously held a joint appointment in the College of Education, University of Illinois at Chicago and in the Faculty of Psychology and Sciences of Education, University of Geneva, Switzerland. Following receipt of her Ph.D. from the University of Michigan in 1965, she was a research fellow under Jean Piaget at the International Center of Genetic Epistemology and the University of Geneva.